CONTINUOUS IMPROVEMENT

CONTINUOUS IMPROVEMENT

Wayne Scott Ross

To Lucy, Thomas, Edward and Isaac at the Ross factory

First published in 2003 by Management Books 2000 Ltd
Forge House, Limes Road
Kemble, Cirencester
Gloucestershire, GL7 6AD, UK
Tel: 0044 (0) 1285 771441/2
Fax: 0044 (0) 1285 771055
E-mail: m.b.2000@virgin.net
Web: mb2000.com

Printed and bound in Great Britain by Biddles, Guildford

British Library Cataloguing in Publication Data is available

ISBN 1-85252-427-8

Contents

Introduction

First off, this book is not going to prophesise and proclaim how great kaizen and lean production are. I know how great they are, and if you've bought this book, then you probably have a very good idea also, or are keen to find out. What this book is going to do is give a brief introduction to the reasons, tools and methods involved, with a minimum of fuss and a lot of RCL, which stands for Red Crayon Language. Basically the sort of writing and language that you see on pictures that children draw. Very simple.

There are many other books on the market, written by great business gurus and Japanese experts, and – don't get me wrong – these lads know their stuff, but they tell you the clear, clean and sanitised reasons behind the systems without telling you how they work, how to use them and how to introduce them. They are also very good at explaining how multi-nationals have Continuously Improved, which is not much good if you are having trouble making mousetraps in Grimsby. It's like someone telling you that there is such a thing as a jigsaw puzzle without explaining what one actually is. Then they rave on about how good the finished picture is. All the while, you are left wondering what all the little parts are, how they fit together and what the finished picture should actually look like.

In this book, I will quickly take you through the simple reasons behind CI before exploring the basic 'Tools for the Job'. These tools will be used on the various techniques, so an overview is required before commencing rather than during.

After that, we will carefully go through the main parts, the 'Jobs' section, showing what the systems can look like, how they fit together, what information should be gathered, the paperwork requirements, feedback – in effect, all you will need to know in order to implement, monitor and maintain a system. Most of the examples in the Jobs section will be very basic, very easy to follow.

We will also have a quick look at the best ways of introducing complete systems to your workplace, taking CI through to its finished product – Lean Production.

As I come from an engineering and production background, a lot of the examples will be primarily based in these areas. Don't let this stop you from taking the principles to other areas. I've taken them from the automotive to the food industry. If I can do that, there is no reason why you shouldn't take them from production to accounts or sales.

After you've read this book of course.

Wayne Scott Ross
April 2003

A Brief History

For a number of years now, Western companies have increasingly been turning to a management system developed by the Japanese that goes by the name of ***Lean Production***. This is very simply a concerted effort to reduce waste in the workplace. By waste, we do not mean scrap or rework parts only, we mean every type of waste, be it time, poor quality or inventory.

In 1945, for various reasons, the Japanese industrial base was non-existent. The Toyoda family controlled a small company that was called Toyota. If they were to pick up after the War where they were in 1939, a drastic and radical approach was needed. Fortunately for them, they employed a young engineer called Taiichi Ohno, a man whose ideas and philosophies were to alter the shape of world-wide industry for ever.

Ohno realised that if Toyota were to become competitive once again, they would have to choose one of two routes – either invest heavily in machinery that wasn't obtainable with money that wasn't available, or to make do with what they had. Obviously they chose the latter.

Ohno's ideas were simple. For instance, Toyota wanted to make two separate and distinct products but only had the machinery to make one, namely a large sheet press. Ohno realised that this press would have to be used for both, but didn't know how. Before the War, the press would have run continually for days or even weeks without stopping, filling stores with car body panels. The main reason for this was the amount of time required to change from one product to the next. With a bit of thought and some smart engineering, Ohno reduced the changeover time to practically nothing, thereby allowing more flexibility from the press. He also introduced a system whereby the press would only run if there was a demand for the component it produced, this production being triggered by a set level in the stores. These principles were named SMED, (Single Minute Change of Dies) and Kanban, the latter being Japanese for 'advertisement'. (The kanban advertised the fact that a certain component was needed.) This reduced the machine base required and the amount of storage space required. It also ensured that if there were defects with the component there would only be perhaps two days' stock that would have to be scrapped or reworked as opposed to two months' stock.

Over time, these ideas and many more were developed by Ohno, and are still being developed by Toyota. The first companies in the west to make a use of these all belonged to the Danaher Group, starting in 1987. After months of harassing a firm of Japanese consultants, including company Vice-Presidents flying over to Japan and sitting in office receptions for days on end, the Japanese finally agreed over a meal in Hartford, Connecticut, to help the Danaher Group. They made one condition – as soon as the meal was finished, they would drive to the nearest Danaher factory and start immediately. They did, arriving on site at two in the morning. After wandering around for an hour or so, they demanded that the factory layout be altered there and then, and to show good faith, the Japanese started to move machinery themselves. To the horror of all watchers, the Japanese showed that it is possible to move a 10 tonne machine using a few shovels and a bit of engineering savvy. The results from the first area they worked in were amazing, with a 50% increase in efficiency by the end of the day.

Ohno became a guru to huge sections of the Industrialised West, mainly in the automotive industry, and when he died in 1990 his ideas and philosophies were providing a secure and stable base for some of the world's biggest and best known names – Rolls Royce Aerospace, Porche, General Electric, Pratt and Whitney, Danaher Tool Group, Tesco, Procter and Gamble, to name but a few. A large number of these organisations don't restrict themselves to in-house events and analysis but actively encourage and help their suppliers to take advantage of the savings that can be made.

Industry abounds with stories, each of which can be checked, of vast improvements in a company's capabilities – a Rover Group supplier who took a complete line changeover from 8 hours to 29 seconds, an automotive supplier who cut costs at their Welsh plant by £6M, year on year for 5 years, a German sports car manufacturer reducing concept to launch time from 7 to 3 years.

Lean Production works. If there are any doubts about this ask yourself one simple question – what happened to the British car and motor bike industry?

Before we start

When I first wrote this book I started off with over a dozen separate pieces of paper that I have used throughout the years in a number of guises for all of the various techniques that are covered in the following pages.

Although there is an initial need for a deal of paperwork where Continuous Improvements are concerned, I have consolidated all these disparate articles into **one single sheet**. Therefore, the need to carry around with you a wad of master copies of this and that has been eliminated.

They have been designed to slip into a clip board for use there and then, being real, active shop-floor tools.

We will look at a blank copy of this sheet overleaf, the first page being the front of the sheet and the second page being the rear, reference sheet. In this day and age of computers and photo-copiers it shouldn't be too difficult to create a double sided sheet.

When analysing the various situations simple circle the 'Sheet Type' name at the top and refer to the rear of the sheet for the various headings that should be used, writing them in the first, un-numbered blank row at the top of the table.

Remembering that these sheets are under copyright, you will no doubt be creating your own working copies, perhaps a separate and distinct item for each of the projects mentioned herein.

Whatever, make sure that you are comfortable with them and understand the various nuances before you try to impress anyone with your new found knowledge.

Sheet type - Kaizen, Single Task, Repetitive Task, Combination Sheet, Location, Problem Listing and Pareto, Time Observation

Location: Observer: Process:

Date: Observation: Component:

Time:

Sheet Type	1	2	3	4	5	6-17
Kaizen	Numbered	Concerns and proposed solution	Trustee	Completion Date	Hit or Miss	'Future Actions'
Single Task	Numbered	Description	Running time	Element Time	Int. or Ext.	'Individual Element Plot' and Graph
Repet. Task	Numbered	Description and Observations			Average Time	Times – running on top, element below
Comb. Sheet	Numbered	Description	Manual ———	Automatic	Walking ———	'Time', Diagram
Location	Numbered	Descriptions				'Scale' and Graph
Problem listing and Paretto	Numbered	Concerns, measured as individuals				6-10, Dates and Quantity, 11-17 is Graphical
Time Observation	Date and Time	Description and Comments	C/O Time	Observer		'Changeover Time', 'Units' and Graph
Time Observation for CEDAC	Date and Time	Comments	Observer	%/Shift		'Units', % Graph

Why Bother With CI?

Look at the following:

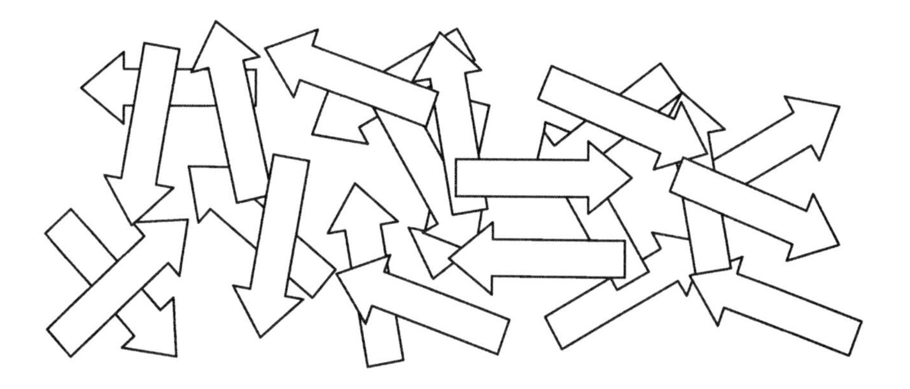

At present, your organisation may look like the arrows, lots of little projects and events being carried out throughout the plant. Ideally, what you would like to see is this:

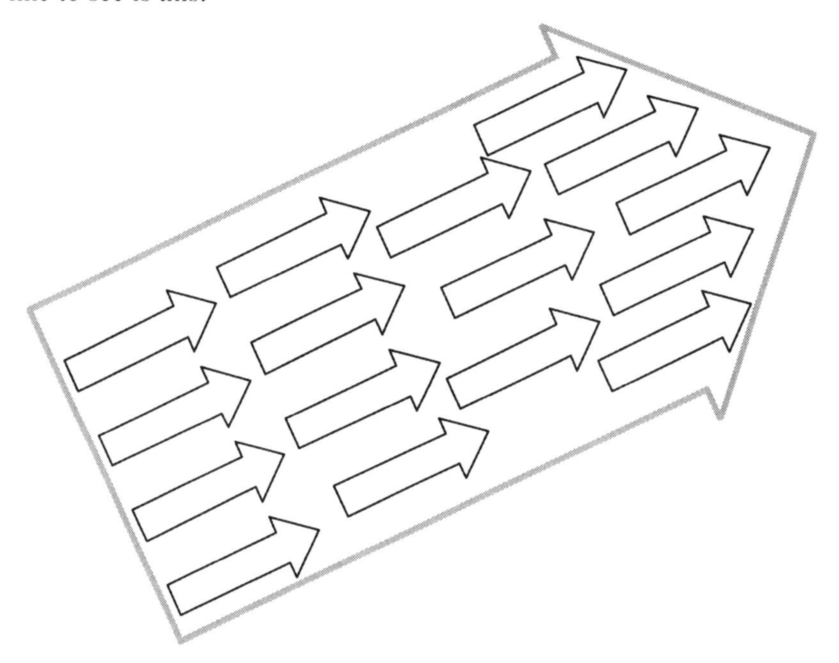

All improvement activities are focused and integrated into the bigger picture.

Non value adding **Value adding**

A series of research programmes by a consultancy group came to a remarkable conclusion – 95% of all effort and actions put into a component as it moves through a factory are Non Value Added. Only 1 in 20 actions actually add value to a product. I didn't believe this until after I'd carried out my own analysis. In the first case I looked at, out of 104 clear and separate actions carried out from goods in to goods out, 97 added no value whatsoever.

Ask yourselves this question for actions:

Would our customers be willing to pay money for that?
... every time a component is moved?
... every time re-work is produced?
... every time an item is stored?

What are we going to achieve by reading this book?

We are going to introduce **Continuous Improvement** activities to the plant, which in turn will lead to **Lean Production**. In many instances these days, CI. activities go by the Japanese name 'Kaizen'. And how would we describe kaizen?

Kaizen two Japanese words, 'Kai' meaning 'Change', and 'Zen' meaning 'For the Better'. Generally taken to mean 'Continuous Improvement' in the modern business world.

Kaizen activities A series of short, very focused events taking place at all levels and involving all aspects of the company and the workforce. Designed to be hard hitting, they form the basic hands-on approach of improvements, but are equally important when they provide support for long term projects.

Lean Production A manufacturing process that has an absolute minimum of waste present.

How are we as a team going to go about achieving this?
Firstly, let's have a look at a few reasons for and against introducing a CI system. The second set, the 'For' column, may look a bit familiar :-

Against	***For***
Expensive	**Expensive**
Time and effort	**Time and effort**
Creates responsibility	**Creates responsibility**
Number crunching	**Number crunching**
Paperwork	**Paperwork**
If it's not broken ...	**If it's not broken ...**

You may be puzzled by this. However, the two columns are both extremely valid. Both contain reasons obtained from people who have expressed opinions on the subject. However, the only difference is:

'If it's not broken ... don't fix it.'

... a rather historical way of looking at things. As CI engineers, we should be saying ...

'If it's not broken ... then make it better.'

Let's look at each of these in a slightly more understandable manner.

Expensive

Short term expense is incurred, creating long term improvements and savings. You must get away from the mind-set that to spend money is a big no-no. Expense is often looked at as also being incurred when a production line is stopped. Get away from thinking about the 3Ps – Production, Production, Production. This attitude has probably done more damage to industry than a whole decade of industrial dispute and bad management plans.

Time and effort

Of course, time and effort are required. People have to be trained, coached and led, until they are in a position to initiate kaizen events and improvements themselves. Analysis is required of the areas that are to be tackled. How else are you going to know exactly what is required? How will you know how much you have improved? Kaizen takes time – for ever in fact – otherwise it wouldn't form the basis of CI, but to actually get your work place to a level where events are self generating requires constant attention in the early stages. Take it from me, it is worth every minute.

Creates responsibility

This is often quoted as being a negative thing. We should not even grace this attitude with a reply.

Number crunching

How else do you know what is accurately happening? How else can you judge your improvements? How else do you begin to know if previous efforts are still working as efficiently as when they were initiated? There has to be valid and accurate feedback from all of the events, and each of the main philosophies should not be put in place as stand-alone events, but should have monitoring systems and periodic reviews. More on this later.

Paperwork

By this, I also refer to computer work. There must be standards. Standards are the building blocks of society, never mind quality and production systems. Without standards, there would be anarchy. And these standards must be clearly defined, clearly displayed and clearly adhered to. In order to do this, paperwork has to be generated. In addition to this, as we are looking at continuous improvements, we must have references to what went before. Therefore, records must be kept of previous events, letting us know if we are running down blind alleys or if there are now reasons why we should follow a particular path that was not deemed suitable in the past.

So, as previously stated :-

If it's not Broken ... then make it better.

Finally – what is the goal of the company, the bottom line?

In the vast majority of cases where major tax avoidance is not a consideration, the goal of the company is :-

- **to make money**
- **to make a profit**

(Yes, we know that some books may disagree with this, where considerations such as return on investment, customer enticement, loss leaders and so on form some of the main storylines, however let's all just agree that if we don't make money, we don't have a job, and leave the R.o.I. to the accountants.)

What is profit?

Traditionally, this fits into the general business equation at the end:

Selling Price = Cost + Profit

However, as profit seems to be the main driver of most businesses, why isn't it at the front? You should look at it as:

Profit = Selling Price – Cost

As the selling price is generally determined by the market, there is very little room for improvement in this area, however if we take the viewpoint that

Profit = Selling Price – Cost

then obviously, if there was no cost, then all of your selling price would also be your profit. Not totally realistic, we agree. However, it is a pointer in the correct direction. How do we start moving in this direction? With a strategic approach to the manufacturing process, we can drastically reduce our costs.

The biggest improvements in cost reduction can be obtained from the following problem areas:

- raw materials
- over engineering
- the 7 wastes of manufacturing (Or is it 8? Possibly 9).

Raw materials

This is where a good purchasing department is worth more than its weight in gold. Recent research has shown that a yearly review and audit of suppliers as far as supply costs are concerned is equivalent to a 6% increase in turnover.

There is the case of the cake manufacturer who decided to remove gelatine from their products. It was traditionally used in the days when most cakes stood around on platters or in warm kitchens, before the mass arrival of fridges. They carried out a recipe review, removed gelatine from the vast majority of their products, saving the business in the region of £120k per annum. An added advantage was that the product became entirely vegetarian, opening up a whole new section of the market place.

Over-engineering

Modern engineers do not carry out the *traditional* factoring for safety – 'Double it and add 10%'. Unfortunately, most sectors of industry still think this way.

If it's solid, it'll last. If it looks good, it is good. If the item will do the job, and do the job well, what more can you want?

There needs to be a lot more thought going into engineering – innovative approaches to basic designs.

Too many people are willing to say:

'We've done cost reduction.'

'This won't help.'

'Reduce cost, reduce quality.'

(Incidentally, there is another old engineering saying to go with the' double it and add 10%'. If engineers are having trouble with a bit of machinery, you will find that one of the most touted solutions is to hit it very hard and swear at it a lot.)

Where we must concentrate within manufacturing plants is in the final problem area –

The 7 wastes of manufacturing

1. Poor Quality
2. Panic Production
3. Time
4. Movement 1 – Parts
5. Movement 2 – People
6. Stock
7. Processing

(And one that is not considered – 8. Poor use of workforce ideas and experience)

Poor Quality

Don't let it happen. Very easy to say, and you will see that it is also very easy to accomplish.

- Create standards and stick to them.
- Focus on problem areas through the use of solid and accurate information.
- Solve at the simplest levels – use the **5 Whys**
- Take time, don't rush in with the first idea.
- Put effort into solving it, a bit of thought.
- Nip it in the bud. Don't let it carry on until every component is effected.
- Engineer it so it can't happen. Introduce **Poka-yoke** to your systems.
- Ask for ideas and solutions from the operators directly involved in the process.
- Create a sense of ownership and pride in the workplace:

'Your work area, your responsibility.'

Above all, don't fire fight. Be pro-active rather than re-active. (Pro-active basically means before the event, before the problem arises. Re-active means that the running around and panicking that you are doing is in reaction to the event. Too late, the problem is already alive.)

It may sound at first like the usual management speak, 'solve the problem before it happens.'

'How do you expect me to do that?' you may ask. Well, we have just shown you a very basic list of recommendations.

A very important item – poor quality is also relevant from your suppliers. I am still amazed that a large number of companies do not keep track of the levels of poor components that are supplied to them. If you have a problem in this area, let your supplier know. Return all unusable items to them and ask for a credit note. If your people have fitted a bad component, have a word with whoever fitted it regarding additional quality training and/or Poka-Yoke systems and bill your supplier for the cost involved in reworking the item. If the item is missed and actually ends up in the hands of a customer, once again review the situation regarding quality and training and bill your supplier for ten times the amount that you billed them for previously. They will soon come around to your way of thinking.

Consider offering to review their manufacturing processes for them from the point of view of a CI engineer. You may then be in a position to ask for half of any cost savings that you come up with.

Panic production

As part of our continuing campaign against the 3Ps, take a look at the following and ask yourself how stupid they seem.

> 'I've got an operator doing nothing. I'll get him to make this because we'll be using it sometime.'
>
> 'They're a difficult product. If we make a few thousand more, it'll save us time in the future.'
>
> 'I need it yesterday. Stop what you're doing and make it now.'
>
> 'There isn't an awful lot in stock so I thought that I'd top the level up a bit.'
>
> 'We're a bit tight for space so I thought that I'd clear some room for raw materials.'

The last two are particularly stupid. Production people do seriously keep a line running just so they don't have to put part batches of raw material back into stores. (If it wasn't all needed, why did they make or order it in the first place?) As for 'topping up the level a bit', consider the following.

There was a metal-bashing company who were part of the very first corporation outside Japan to be involved in kaizen and lean production. As part of this corporation, they were involved in a series of senior visits/kaizen weeks every year from both Japanese consultants and corporation Vice Presidents. One of these visits/kaizen events was to re-arrange the layout of the goods-out area. It was discovered that for one item they held 25 years worth of stock. (That's *twenty five* years.)

All of the above quotes result in false economies. The attitudes expressed come about through not enough information in the system, not enough number crunching, not enough planning and, our favourite because it is never mentioned in any factory, poor management.

The last item to mention here is the amount of money invested by production to make parts that are not required. You have added value to those parts, only for them to sit in a storage area. In effect, all that you have done is place money onto the shelves and nothing more.

Time

Let's start with a little list of where we waste time.

- people waiting for parts
- lost time due to changeovers

- lost time due to breakdowns
- lost time due to any one of a dozen reasons, such as waiting for machines to come up to speed, temperature, pressure ...

This is a huge area for improvement. **SMED, TPM** and **Standard Work Analysis** form the basis for this.

However, time is not just a case of how long the machines are running for, but also a case of how good their performance is when they are running. In addition to this, the amount of time that can be gained from machinery, not by speeding it up but by analysing the areas of waste in the cycle, can be tremendous.

A company with what was once a purpose built and state-of-the-art packing hall decided to carry out a review of all line speeds with a view to speeding them up. It was decided from the outset that the packing hall was the main bottleneck, as they had tried running the machines faster but the increase in damaged and poor quality parts was greater than the added throughput. It was decided that all 8 case packers would have to be replaced at a cost of nearly £1M. Their kaizen engineer heard of this and spent one hour with a stop watch, paper, pen and calculator before deciding that an extra 37% was available from one or two simple changes. These included replacing the in-feed belt with one that had a greater co-efficient of friction, as there was a 3 second difference between the top and bottom layers of product entering the machine due to the bottom layer being pushed into the machine by a build up of product that the top layer didn't have. This was three seconds from an 11 second cycle time.

Once again, not enough time and effort is put into solving these problems. There is also the added problem that people like to spend large amounts of company money if they think that they can justify it. Makes them feel big. They probably drive shiny red sports cars as well.

Movement 1 – Parts

Moving parts does not add value to them. Quite the opposite. You pay someone to move them, you pay for equipment for that person to use when they move them. If parts are being moved, you are not even considering the possibility of cellular manufacturing. And don't think that the answer is to purchase a lot of conveyors, hundreds of feet in length. A good stock system, **kanban**, to keep components to a minimum for instance, and cellular manufacturing may be what you need.

In addition to this, it takes time to move parts, therefore in order to keep the factory running you need to increase the amount of WIP on the shop floor. This ties up more capital and space, with the added danger of components being damaged or degrading as they sit around waiting to be put to good use.

Movement 2 – People

If all operators spent eight hours of an eight hour day at their positions, all production managers and directors would be happy. We all know however that an eight hour day is not eight hours long. Consider tea and lunch breaks, whether official or not, smoke breaks, visits to the toilets, going in search of a newspaper, talking to Billy about last nights tv.

However, what none of us stop to think about is the amount of time wasted when that person has to move, say, two metres from one work station to the next. Now if they only do that once then it's not really worthwhile moving plant or machinery for the sake of a few seconds there and a few seconds back.

What if they have to do it for every operation?

That's when we start to reap the benefits of basic **Standard Work Analysis**. Look at the following.

If the cycle time for a component is 60 seconds around a work cell and the operator spends two seconds walking between, let us say just two of the machines in the cell, then every hour they have wasted 120 seconds, or two components. That is sixteen components in an eight hour day, 90 components a week and 4,320 in a 48 week year. Another way is to say that 3% has been lost, only it is never looked at as actually being lost due to the fact that the cell may well be producing at the standard rate set for it. Remember the example about the case packing machine? – similar situation. Watch what is happening, analyse and act.

Nissan carried out an analysis on walking distance on their main assembly line in Sunderland for one assembly station. They reduced the operators walking distance from 12 to 6 steps, converted that to time saving and calculated that this was equivalent to £125,000 per year in lost contribution.

Movement of people also means items such as reaching, stretching, bending and the like, with all of the associated Health and Safety, Repetitive Strain Injury issues and the like.

Stock

If you have £5 million tied up in stock, what good is it doing you? Nothing. You may still occasionally see adverts on television or in the papers proclaiming the merits of a showroom or such like, which carry a legend along the lines of – 'Over 5 million bricks to choose from.'

Now, we don't know the current value of your common brick, but rest assured that if you went to your company accountant with a briefcase full of money to the equivalent value of the bricks, the last thing that he would do is leave it lying around in the yard. He may consider the Maldives and a numbered account in Switzerland for a few minutes, but will probably opt for the High Yield Account.

- Think of the capital tied up there that could be used elsewhere.
- Think of the interest on 5 million bricks' worth of money.
- Think of the shelf life.
- What about damage to packaging?
- Oil, dust and grime accumulating?
- Is quality suffering?
- Your warehouse is heated, lit and signposted.

Not all entirely relevant to bricks, I admit, but you must realise that if you carry stock, you carry costs. The greater the stock, the greater the costs.

Stock doesn't increase in value, not generally anyway.

Processing

This ties up a number of different situations, some of which to be honest have already been mentioned. For instance, your workers walking two metres every time they have to carry out an operation. There are a lot of sections that interact with each other, so an improvement in one area may lead to an improvement in another. As far as processing is concerned, we want to look at the actual component, so:

- Determine the best routing of parts.
- Evaluate the order the operations.
- Can continuous flow be introduced? One piece flow? (Nearly always yes, in one form or another.)
- Is it feasible to introduce manufacturing cells?

Analyse the waste in the system – can operation two start before operation one has fully finished? Can actuator three start when actuator four moves away from the component rather than when it reaches its 'home' location? A second here and a second there.

(Wasted Ideas and Experience)

This is an add-on, something that few books or companies mention. However, it is the main building block of kaizen. The whole principle of CI is that you involve the workforce, as they are the people who can tell you the how, why and where of waste, problems, safety issues, concerns, and if only one person with twenty years' experience is allowed to implement some of the ideas that they have stored up or locked away for that period of time, then that is a start, but when the entire workforce can act together as a team, co-ordinating and pulling ideas, implementing them and foreseeing problem areas, then all the better. When that day arrives, you will be nearing the end of a journey that has opened your eyes and mind forever.

We've had a look at the thinking behind CI and lean production, the many reasons for and the reasons against (none), the three areas where costs can be reduced, and an analysis of the various types of waste. Where to from here?

What is there in a Lean Production System that you can introduce?

Firstly, the tools for the job

1. **CPE** – measuring your efficiencies
2. **Takt time** – what time is your customer giving you to manufacture?
3. **Kaizen Monthly** – keeping tabs on it all
4. **5 Whys** – determining the root cause of the issues
5. **Pareto analysis** – easy on the eye visuals and information gathering
6. **Process flow chart** – the difference between 'what is' and 'what should'.

After that, the Jobs

1. **5S** – 'A place for everything and everything in its place.'
2. **TPM** – keeping it all running smoothly

3. **SMED** – changeover time reduction
4. **Poka-Yoke** – foolproofing
5. **CEDAC** – problem solving
6. **FMEA** – eliminating the problems before they occur
7. **Standard Work** – the best way of making it
8. **Kanban** – visual stock control

It is advisable that the jobs be implemented in the order shown above, for a few very simple reasons. **5S** gives you the basics that you need – it is a good housekeeping exercise, removes clutter, and if you are in the fortunate position of having a world class expert visit you, they will not do anything until you can show that you have fully grasped the 5S philosophy. One of the reasons for **SMED** is to reduce stockholdings, and if you have no stock and a major breakdown, then you are in trouble. **TPM** will help prevent breakdowns.

As you by now should have increased throughput, you must look to reduce poor quality components. **Poka-Yoke** is a foolproofing device and will contribute towards this goal. In addition it can be considered a tool for **CEDAC** and will therefore make CEDAC easier. This in turn provides a solid base and experience for the design of **FMEA** systems.

Standard Work entails the pulling together of details from all these systems as you look to operate an integrated and efficient workplace. And finally, just to make sure that you are not going to run out of components for your customers, **Kanban** looks to reduce your stock. However, we have put it at the end just to ensure that all is well and good before committing yourself. Belt and Braces.

Tools for the Job

CPE – Complete Plant Efficiency

CPE is also becoming widespread under a different name – Overall Equipment Effectiveness. However, in this instance, we will continue to call it CPE.

This is by far and away the most accurate method of determining how the factory is performing. A lot of senior management look at a lot of different figures, be they machine and/or operator efficiencies, quantity of components produced, machine uptime, delivery targets, whatever.

Where CPE gains an advantage over all of these various methods is through the fact that it considers *all* aspects of production.

There is no point in a machine running at 100% 'efficiency' if 10% of what is produced is of such poor quality that it can not be sold. Likewise, if there is no downtime recorded, it doesn't help if the machinery is only producing 80% of the components it should have produced in a given time period.

(How can this happen? Operators may have small problems that are not necessarily recorded as downtime but still eat into production, for instance stopping a machine to oil a bearing, go to the toilet, load a hopper, clear a blockage.)

Look at the following six reasons that cause the three main distinctions in poor plant efficiency.

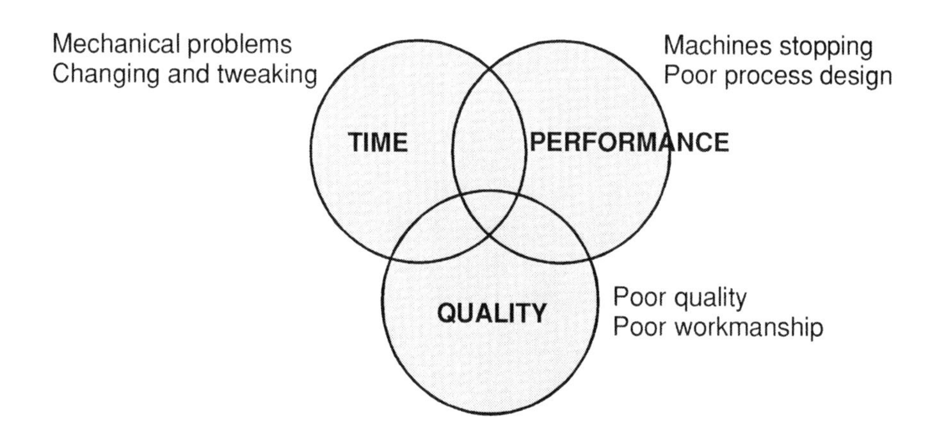

When all of these areas are included in the overall picture, it can clearly be seen that the only section where good quality components are being made is where the three circles come together. This may seem extreme, but if you consider the alternatives methods of measurement, then CPE gives a clear and concise picture with all parameters included.

How do we calculate the figure? Simple. We follow the next few steps.

$$\text{Time} = \frac{\text{Available Production Time} - \text{Downtime}}{\text{Available Production Time}} \times 100\%$$

$$\text{Performance} = \frac{\text{Cycle Time} \times \text{Amount Processed}}{\text{Operating Time}} \times 100\%$$

$$\text{Quality} = \frac{\text{Processed Amount} - \text{Defects}}{\text{Processed Amount}} \times 100\%$$

These simple equations will allow you to easily calculate each of the main issues that senior management should look at to try and get a feel for how the factory is operating.

The secret is to combine them, using the final figure as a measure of complete plant efficiency.

CPE = Time x Performance x Quality

With this method, you are going to obtain figures that are a lot lower than previously calculated. If all of the above individual areas are calculated at 95% efficiency, with CPE this will drop to 86%.

As an example of performance:

$$\text{Performance} = \frac{\text{Cycle Time} \times \text{Amount Processed}}{\text{Operating Time}} \times 100\%$$

If you run a machine for one hour, and the cycle time of each component is exactly one second, you would expect to make 3,600 components in one hour. This obviously equates to 100% efficiency.

If, however, in the hour you only produce 3,000 components, then efficiency can be calculated as follows:

$$\text{Performance} = \frac{1 \times 3{,}000}{3{,}600} \times 100\%$$

= 83%

It is important to remember that times must be like for like, that is if you use seconds for cycle time, then seconds must be used for operating time.

An addition to the above may also be considered. Some companies may want to introduce a fourth measurement of how well they supply their customers, expressed as a percentage and added to the overall equation.

CPE = Time x Performance x Quality x Delivery

This will possibly take the overall figure lower still, but the information obtained will highlight the problem areas and drive improvements through.

What the delivery figure will not do is increase the efficiency. If the delivery figure is above 100%, this is false accounting. You may think that delivering early is a good thing, hence the extra efficiency, however the knock-on effects to your customers may be detrimental to their operations.

An additional reminder – as you increase the working capacity of the factory through SMED, TPM and the like, your CPE figure will increase dramatically. Direct comparisons between 'before' and 'after' will be difficult if you are forever altering the CPE base line after every CI initiative or when it breaches the 100% mark. You may want to consider comparing 'silly' figures, for instance a before of 82% and an after of 138%, with a yearly alteration of the figures. The 132% at the end of 2003 becomes the 100% at the start of 2004.

Takt Time

Strangely enough, the 'Concrete Heads' in Germany have contributed to the Lean Production philosophy also. (They are called 'Concrete Heads' by a lot of the Japanese Kaizen Masters due to their set ways and being adverse to change.)

'Takt' is a German word referring to musical timing, the beat if you like.

Therefore, Takt Time is the beat that production must follow if it wants to keep up. In effect, the amount of time that you have to fulfil your customer demands. For instance, if the customer wants a part every second, then the Takt time is one second.

It gives a quick indication of whether the factory, cell, production line, whatever, can cope with the demand placed on it.

It can be used in the construction of cells or production lines where a simple calculation between Cycle Time and Takt Time will let you know at a glance if you have the capacity.

Takt Time is generally calculated in the following manner.

$$\textbf{TAKT time} = \frac{\textbf{Seconds/time period}}{\textbf{Demand/time period}}$$

For instance, if you wanted to run only one product in a cell continuously, the takt time for one year would possibly be calculated like this :-

Seconds/year = Number of hours actually worked per week
x 60 Minutes
x 60 Seconds
x Number of weeks worked per year
= Number of seconds worked per year

For example, a 37-hour week, spread within a 46-week working year, would produce a figure of 6,127,200 seconds per year.

Pieces per time period is actually your customer's demands – for instance, they require 6,127,200 components per year.

If used correctly, Takt Time can be a very useful tool for the planning and implementation of ideas into the work place.

Remember though, a calculation must be made for downtime through changeovers, maintenance, breakdown etc, and the calculation incorporated for actual running efficiency. You may actually have 6,127,200 seconds a year, however the CPE figure will affect your cycle time, leading to a reduction in perceived capacity.

Therefore,

If your customers require 6,127,200 components per year then the Takt Time = 1

If your customers require 12,254,400 components per year then the Takt Time = 0.5

If your customers require 3,063,600 components per year then the Takt Time = 2

So what does this tell us?

As TT and CT are both measured in the same units (TT = Takt Time and CT = Cycle Time), namely seconds per component, then direct comparisons can be made.

1. If TT > CT then production can cope with the demand.
2. If TT = CT then production is breaking even.
3. If TT < CT then production will have to catch up.

In the case of number 3, this can be achieved by double shifting, utilising more machinery or manpower. This may be false accounting however.

Three ways of doing it, yes, but what you really need to do is increase the CPE figures through greater utilisation of kaizen methods. In some extreme cases, you may have to increase working hours or invest heavily in new capital plant, but initially the easiest and most effective way is to increase CPE and throughput.

In the case of throughput, this can be tackled with careful analysis of the working methods applied, and is covered in the section on Work Standardisation.

Kaizen Monthly

The role of the Kaizen Monthly – essentially a newspaper of informative bulletin – is to document every action that is carried out during an exercise and to keep a note of all outstanding actions. By every action we mean *every* action, whether successful or not. (Yes, sometimes we do fail, although 'a re-appraisal of our objectives' is more in keeping with management speak.) This is particularly important six months after the event is completed when you return to the same area to carry out another event. The last thing that you want is to start duplicating an unsuccessful action.

Likewise, if something was tried out without success, the reasons why it was unsuccessful may no longer be relevant, therefore try it once again. You will only know this if you have clear and concise information.

Outstanding issues must be carried out within one month of the exercise ending. Hence the name. There has to be a time period that we can follow, a standard if you like, and Kaizen Monthly not only has a nice ring to it, but will keep outstanding issues alive and help to push them through. This also ensures that there is a definite finishing date, otherwise the outstanding issues will continue to be outstanding until they are forgotten about, and that attitude is no good to anyone.

How is it implemented?

It is vitally important that each member of the review team should be in possession of up-to-date Newspapers, obtained from either the person who submitted the Newspaper or the designated CI engineer, detailing the state of play at that moment in time.

At the review meetings, the team will discuss any outstanding actions that have been signed off and actions from new Kaizen Monthly Newspapers will be allocated. By discussing, we mean that a simple 'hit' or 'miss' will do. If it is a 'hit', good. If it is a 'miss', then what are you going to do to bring it back into the time schedule? Discuss, shout, allocate. Yes, you can shout because the road to CI and Lean Production will not be dug up just because one individual cannot be bothered to carry out the work allocated or because someone is afraid to have his or her voice heard.

Once an action is completed, a line should be clearly drawn in green highlighter pen through that action. This gives a clear indication that the action has been completed. Likewise, if the action is not completed in the allocated time, then a red circle should be highlighted around the name of the person allocated to that action to show that they are falling behind.

Once the review meeting is completed, the Newspapers should be posted in the various areas where you have set up the CI Information boards to inform the workforce what the state of play is.

All Newspapers should be posted on these boards to let everyone see what is happening with regards to not only exercises they were a part of but to other exercises in the rest of the work place.

At the next review meeting, completed actions should not feature on the newspaper. This serves two main purposes – it reduces the visible size of the Kaizen Monthly and promotes a feeling that the actions are being carried out.

What the Newspaper does not do is act as a wish list for maintenance issues. This may seem obvious at first, however, you will find that in time they will develop into this purpose if you do not keep on top of the team and focus their attention on the CI event. If there are major maintenance issues, why? Get onto the maintenance department and get these issues sorted out.

The Kaizen Monthly stays in print until all of the actions are completed.

So, what does it actually look like?

The following is an example of a partially filled in Kaizen Monthly Newspaper.

Sheet type - Kaizen, Single Task, Repetitive Task, Combination Sheet, Location, Problem Listing and Pareto, Time Observation

Location: 45 tonne press | Observer: WSR | Process:
Date: 3 November | Observation: | Component:
Time:

No	Concerns and proposed solution	Trustee	Comp Date	Hit - Miss	Future actions
1	Components on the floor - fit guards to the chutes	WSR	28/11		
2	Tools lying around - make tool rack and fit	LSB	7/11	Miss	Obtain fitter immediately
3	Incomplete set of feed plates Complete the set (Sub-contract?)	FNB	28/11		
4	Machine guards interfering with changeovers fir release	Maint	7/11	Hit	Complete
	and interlock				
5	Lack of proper tooling - purchase required tooling	LSB	2/11		Complete
6	Worn shaft on flywheel - turn a new one	CJB	15/1		

The Kaizen Monthly is completed in the following manner

Location	This is simply the area of the work place that this newspaper covers.
Observer	This should be the Team Co-ordinator who headed up the exercise. Note however that this person does not complete the tasks personally.
Date	The original submission date. Allows us to keep track of the time it takes to complete the Newspaper's actions.
Numbered	Simply 1, 2, 3 etc.
Concerns and Proposed Solutions	The actions that have been or have to be completed. (There are no problems, just opportunities.)
Trustees	Who the actions are assigned to.
Completion Date	The date that the action will be completed by. Traditionally this date refers to a Friday. (Don't leave it to the last day of the Kaizen month.)
Hit or Miss	Were we successful?
Future Actions	If it was a Miss what is proposed to make it a Hit before the month is up?

As can be seen from Action 6, there are some items that are impossible to complete within the month due to lead-times from suppliers, tooling times, special finishing on items (heat treat and the like).

In cases such as this it is something that we have to learn to live with. They are Special Cases, outwith our control.

As soon as they are back within our control, they are completed immediately.

5 Whys

This is simply asking questions that get to the heart of the problem. Although the number 5 is used, you should keep asking until you are sure that you have found the root cause.

There is no point in identifying a problem only to take one step back down the line to rectify it if the root cause is four steps away.

You should act like a little five-year old until you are happy with the situation. For instance:

Why did he slip and break his arm? *There was oil on the floor.*
Why was there oil on the floor? *The drip tray leaks.*
Why does the drip tray leak? *It's full to overflowing.*
Why is it full? *The sump leaks.*
Why does the sump leak? *It's cracked.*
Why is it cracked? *It was hit by a fork lift.*

What do you do then? You repair the crack, and then worry about your fork lift drivers. Do they need better training? Should a barrier be erected around the sump? Can the machine be moved to a safer area? You have to decide on a course of action to prevent the incident re-occurring.

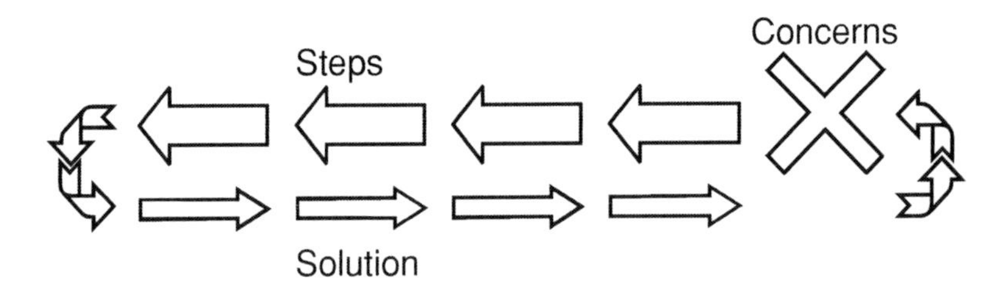

Obviously someone saw that there was a problem at one time, and asked the question 'Why is there oil on the floor?', but that was the only question they asked and so the solution that they came up with was a quick fix. It was probably more expensive and time consuming to incorporate the drip tray and its associated emptying over a period of time than it was to fix the leak, but it wasn't thought through enough.

The simple example above is the only reason for the 5 Why approach – to arrive at the root cause. Or indeed, causes. There doesn't have to be only one reason. There may be a branching off two or three steps down the line and the root cause came from two separate areas.

Is there anything strange about the above example? Have a look again.

There are not 5 questions, but 6. Just because it is called 5 Whys doesn't mean that you are only allowed 5 questions. Take as many as you like, just so long as you get to the root cause.

Apart from Arabia a few thousand years ago, I have no idea where the figure 5 came from, but I am fairly sure that after a large amount of research and money, someone decided that there are only five steps to solving any problem, five levels of separation. Well, statistically that may be, but we are looking at the real world. Ask as many questions as you want or need.

The above scenario can be a typical version of events. By simply backtracking through the problems, you can source the root cause. In this case, not only have you solved a glaring health and safety problem, but think of the savings in oil and the maintenance issue of a machine possibly running without any oil. If you can solve the leak problem, why spend money on a drip tray? They don't even look good, they do not create the sort of impression that you want to show a prospective or current customer.

If an operator is emptying the tray, he is not watching or operating the machine. If it is decided that a fork lift truck driver is in need of extra training, then even better.

I used to use the above example as an exaggerated story to get the message over with an emphasis on safety. It was always stressed that this was made up, however after using it for the first time with a new employer, three days later someone did slip and break an arm due to a leaking drip tray.

The questions – who do you ask these to?

In the main, ask the people who are directly involved, the operators, the workers. If you are very lucky, you may have a layer of management above them, chargehands, production controllers and the like who know all of the ins and outs, but the workers are the ones who deal with issues on a daily basis therefore they will give you the best information. They will also tell you how long the problem has been occurring for and how many times they have asked the maintenance department to correct it.

There is one vitally important aspect to all of this though – you can go too far, making solutions totally impractical. You wouldn't consider replacing the sump with a titanium model that would easily withstand a direct hit from a forklift, would you? You may decide to put a forklift barrier around the machinery as well as extra training, to provide belt and braces.

You have to decide on the most practical, cost effective and easily installable solution. That after all is one of the reasons that you are employed – to make decisions.

Pareto analysis

Pareto analysis is very simple, so simple in fact that they teach it to us all in Primary school. It is really no more than gathering information and plotting it on a bar graph, giving an indication of areas where problems are occurring and/or what those problems are.

And to be perfectly honest, the graph itself is purely for communication purposes, as all of the information obviously has to be known before a graph can be constructed. That doesn't mean to say that we can do away with it though, as it provides a very good visual aid.

Once the information has been collected you can start to target the problems dependent on one of the following five reasons:

1. the problem with the greatest frequency
2. the one that will give you the greatest monetary saving
3. the problem that the customer has highlighted as causing them problems – a very important one, this
4. a series of problems that may individually not be too large, but collectively are considered easy to solve and will provide a good, quick hit whilst eliminating a large percentage of the overall total
5. the one that someone with a bit of power has noticed as they walked around one day.

For example:

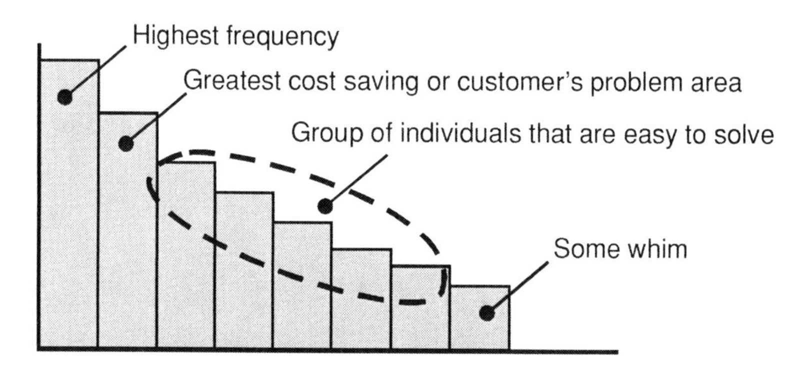

Number five above may sound irrelevant, but you can be sure that if the boss sees something that causes concern, it will be a major issue, even if it happens once in a blue moon and there are other priorities. A little knowledge can be a dangerous thing, for others.

There are two main aspects to Pareto analysis – the actual gathering of the information and the graph itself, both shown on the Problem Listing and Pareto sheet.

Problem Listing and Pareto Sheet (see opposite)

This is designed to highlight three main aspects:

1. details of the problems encountered
2. the quantity of the problems
3. the time period over which the problems occur.

Concerns

These should not be overly specific as individuals, but there should be enough categories to allow for all the problems encountered. As an example, if operating within an area that was producing only one type of component, you would write 'Poor profile under the head' and 'Poor profile along the shank' rather than just 'Poor profile', or 'Shank too long' and 'Head too long' rather than just 'Too long'. (If used across a site for purposes of monitoring scrap levels, then your 'Concerns' may incorporate the names of production areas e.g. Line 1, Finishing Section A etc.)

However, don't write 'Shank too long due to …' and insert a reason. This is not information gathering, this is you thinking that you know the reason, and that is always a dangerous approach as you do not open your mind to other possibilities. You will have the chance to air your views when the project team meets, when the Pareto is used in the problem solving techniques that we will encounter.

The categories are written in as they occur, not written in based on historical records or gut feelings. There are two main reasons for this:

1. People might not highlight a problem if there is a list and that problem is not on the list
2. A problem may not occur until another has happened, therefore if highlighted in the order that they actually appear we are provided with

Sheet type - Kaizen, Single Task, Repetitive Task, Combination Sheet, Location, Problem Listing and Pareto, Time Observation

Location: *Forming cell* | Observer: | Process: *Form, cut, trim, thread*

Date: *November 2003* | Observation: | Component: *M36x150 Cap*

Time:

Number	Concerns, measured as individuals				5th	6th	7th	8th	9th	10	20	30	40	50		Tot
1	Poor head profile				IIIII I	IIIII IIIII I	IIIII III	IIIII II	IIIII III							40
2	Shank too long				III	II	I	I	III							10
3	Shank too short					II	I	II								5
4	Head not concentric about the shank						IIII	I								5
5	Bad thread at head end				IIIII	IIIII	IIIII									15
				Total	14	20	19	11	11							75

additional and accurate information. There is a need for operator awareness here, which is one of the main reasons why operators should be included in all project teams.

Remember the most important part – the reasons for concern, not the causes.

Quantity

You obviously have to know the scale of the problem in order to allocate priorities. For instance, if there was no information on amounts, you may target a problem that is only responsible for perhaps 5% of the overall amount of defects, whilst those producing 95% are left to run.

Having said that, if the information is being gathered in a wide and general area, such as scrap levels over the whole site, rather than within a specific area that may only produce one type of component, then you do not always run with the largest amount.

If for instance, as a factory you produce 10kg of scrap iron per day and only 2kg of scrap gold, which item would you tackle first?

Tick marks are sufficient for measuring this because they allow quick and easy recording. As shown in the example above, the totals for columns and rows all add up – just to be pedantic.

The Time period

This allows a couple of different aspects to be taken into account. One, once again, is the scale of the problem – one bad component a year is bad enough, but one per minute is ruinous. Another aspect is that when further analysis is carried out, the time periods may highlight differences across the various shifts, times of day, times of year. You may want to monitor by the shift rather than by the week. In this respect, accurate recording will highlight areas such as training requirements, machine warm-up times or raw material supply issues.

Remember, these sheets are just examples, so if you want to monitor by the hour, then you would obviously change the time period from 'days' to 'hours', and the amount of columns from 5 to 8 perhaps.

The sheet also shows the relevant information with regards to the specific area, process and component, to allow further analysis and reference at a future date.

Pareto Graph

This allows a very visual and easily understood representation of the problems to be shown. Extremely useful for presentations, notice boards, monitoring of event successes as the event progresses and so on.

It is completed in such a simple manner that I really don't think that I should go into it in any detail. After all, if you can read this, you should be able to figure it out. However, remember to plot the units, whether individual components, kg, lbs.

Flow Sheets and Charts

It can be almost guaranteed that what is happening at present within a given operation or process is not what should be happening. The sequence is wrong. The decisions are wrong. The tooling is wrong. Something somewhere will be out of sync.

The main purpose of the flow chart is to accurately document what is happening at present (actual), and to allow a comparison to be made with what should be happening (ideal). The difference between these two situations is commonly called a 'problem'.

'Ideal' charts can be used for problem solving, as highlighted in the CEDAC section, or merely to provide an overview of a process for training techniques, ISO/Quality documentation, customer/supplier liaison and so on.

Advantages

It is essential that you have clearly documented and defined methods of processing. Flow charts provide these, securing quality and productivity, providing information rather than gut feeling. They remove the 'training with Nellie' scenario, when new operators are left to watch what is happening in the hope that they pick the job up from there.

In addition, flow charts:

- provide a clear diagrammatic display
- clarify the sequence
- show the relationships between the various steps
- identify deviations from the ideal
- help to show where problems are and are not likely to occur
- are very useful in initial training for new operators.

As there is a deal of specialisation in the following charts, I have created them separately from the basic design we have been following up to this moment. There are two main types of charts that are commonly used:

1. The Systems chart

This is used to provide an overview of, obviously, systems, for instance the means by which a new product is introduced or the steps involved in auditing a new supplier. They consist of 7 symbols, each one designed to provide a clear, visual indication of the actions that will be encountered

How is it constructed?

The ideal manner is to follow the process through, detailing on a Systems Flow Sheet the individual operations that are encountered. One of these sheets is shown overleaf. Mark off on the flow sheet a description of the System Step whilst marking down in the boxes what the corresponding category is. For instance, a System Step of 'Create list of requirements' would be placed in the category of 'Gathering'.

If there is a decision to be made, then mark down 'Y' or 'N' in the next set of boxes in the System Flow Sheet and detail the Steps required for each of these decisions. If necessary then draw on the sheet the flow of the decision. An example of this is shown on the Systems Flow Sheet.

Where a 'link' to another system is required, then mark down what that system is and where the relevant information can be found. If information is stored, then make sure that the storage area and method are documented.

As an example of how these all fit together, here are the symbols and a flow sheet showing the steps involved a shopping expedition:

Action	Symbol	Description
Start/stop		This symbol marks the start and finish of the system
Process		Marks where/when an action is carried out
Deciding		Shows when a decision has been reached, for instance, 'accept' or 'reject'
Gathering		Information is brought together here from numerous areas, for instance three team members working on different aspects of the project
Linking		Creates a bridge to another system chart, for instance the steps involved in setting up a new customer account
Filing		Storage of the information, in a database or cabinet
Reporting		Creation of a report

SYSTEM FLOW SHEET

System: *Shopping* Date: *May 2003* Time: *15.30*
Observer: *WSR* Observation: *No 1*

Chert type: ACTUAL / ~~IDEAL~~

Start/stop	Process	Decide	Gathering	Linking	Filing	Report	SYSTEM STEP
●							Start
		●					Is there a need for a shopping list - YES
			●				Review current levels of consumables - kitchen
			●				Review current levels of consumables - bathroom
			●				Review current levels of consumables - rest of house
						●	Create list of requirements
					●		Place list onto fridge with magnet
	●						At allocated time, prepare to go to the shops
				●			Drive to shops - 'System 123, Driving'
	●						Collect goods that are on the list
	●						Pay for goods
					●		Obtain receipt for purchases
				●			Drive home from shops - System 123, Driving'
	●						Place purchases where required
●							Stop

Start/stop Process Decide Gathering
Linking Filing Report

2. The Process Chart

As the name suggests, Process Charts are used to track processes. By processes we mean the sum of the individual operations that are carried out. Operations are made up of 5 clearly defined states, namely:

Action	Symbol	Description
Operation	○	Identifies the main operations within the process, usually where the component has added value to it
Movement	⇨	Shows both kinds of movement - people and parts
Stores	▽	Permanent storage of the components. Can be parts leaving the line to finished goods or raw parts joining the line.
WIP or Delay	D	Temporary storage, between CNC machines, batches waiting for the next step or sub-assemblies waiting for the main body
Inspection	□	QA check, Poka-Yoke, SPC details etc.

By combining these five, any system can be drawn

How is it constructed?

The ideal manner is to follow the process through, detailing on a Process Flow Sheet the individual operations that are encountered. One of these sheets is shown later on. This is to include items such as 'press start button', 'mark component with check paint' and 'place component on table while operator looks for a clean rag'.

If you are mapping a system for general information, then try and detail the operations that occur in every cycle. Therefore, if the operator needs a clean rag only in 1 in 20 cycles or so, this is not a major concern. (What should be the concern is why they need the rag.) If the rag is required in every cycle then it should be included.

However, if you are creating a flow chart as part of a greater event, such as CEDAC, then yes, include the operation of looking for a clean rag. It may be that the problem you are trying to solve has a scrap rate of 5%, or 1 in 20, therefore it is vitally important to include all variations of the theme.

And as an example, let's wash the dishes:

PROCESS FLOW SHEET

Location: *Kitchen* Date: *May 2003* Time: *15.30*
Process: *Washing dishes* Component: *Crockery/cutlery*
Observer: *WSR* Observation: *No 1*
Chart type: ACTUAL / ~~IDEAL~~

○	⇨	▽	D	□	OPERATION
●					Put plug in plug-hole
●					Turn on the taps
●					Fill sink with water
				●	Check water temperature is to within specifications
●					Turn off the taps
	●				Remove washing-up liquid from cupboard
●					Remove lid from washing-up liquid
●					Add washing-up liquid to sink and mix
				●	Ensure there is sufficient washing-up liquid in water
●					Replace lid to washing-up liquid
	●				Replace washing-up liquid in cupboard
	●				Move crockery from cupboard top to sink
●					Wash individual components to QA specifications
			●		Place on draining board
●					Repeat until all crockery is washed
	●				Move cutlery from cupboard top to sink
●					Wash individual components to QA specifications
			●		Place on draining board
●					Repeat until all cutlery is washed
●					Remove plug from plug-hole
			●		Wait until sink is empty
●					Wash down sink
				●	Ensure the sink is clean
	●				Collect towel
				●	Ensure that towel is clean and dry
●					Dry crockery/cutlery components
	●				Move dried components to their storage areas
		●			Place dried components into marked storage areas
	●				Replace towel to drying hook

○ Operation ⇨ Movement ▽ Store D WIP/Delay □ Inspect

The towel and washing up liquid are regarded as tools for the job, therefore are not marked down as being stored. This reference is for components only – parts passing through your factory – in this case a sink.

You will notice also that this flow sheet does not concern itself with items such as what to do with poor quality components. There are no 'Decisions' symbols, so when we say 'Ensure that the towel is clean and dry' we are just highlighting the action of inspecting the towel and not detailing the specifications. (If the towel is not within the specifications laid out by your Quality Team or ISO documentation, then these systems should highlight what steps to take.) In effect, we are tracking the main operations in the process, not the secondary operations.

If we were to follow the operations undertaken when a quality concern to the process came in, where would we stop? Would we follow the operator to the canteen or to the toilet? No, we follow the main operations, and therefore we will have to watch a number of cycles in order to find out what is actually happening.

As a part of this, remember that operators may not follow a common cycle, by which I mean that in one cycle they may go to machine 3 before machine 4 whilst in the next they go to machine 4 before machine 3. Watch and learn.

It will also be noticed that all value-adding operations are marked down as 'Operations', but that not all operations are value adding, for instance 'Turn off the taps' is not value adding. Whilst the operator has to do this and the water is essential for the cleaning process, the operation of turning the taps on does not in itself help to actually clean the dishes.

'Ideal' Sheets

The above examples have concentrated on the 'Actual' side of things. Now is the time to have a very quick look at the 'Ideal' side of things.

The Ideal sheets should be completed in the same manner, but rather than following the operator as they go about their business, they should be completed through a combination of:

- written specifications
- brainstorming
- reference to quality issues
- health and safety matters

- standard work analysis
- in effect whatever the team has decided is the most accurate and suitable form of information available to complete the sheet.

Remember though, as Flow Sheets and Charts are a major part of the CEDAC problem solving technique, as detailed in a later chapter, it may not be too advantageous to tackle the issue of the ideal situation at present. Rather you may wish to hold off completing this until the CEDAC team have reached some conclusions.

Next Step

The size and design of the sheets are ideal for use on the shop floor – they can be easily attached to a flip board, stored in a day book or whatever. But once these sheets are completed, you can if you wish (and I recommend that you do) transfer the information to a larger diagram that shows the symbols as the main focus of attention, making it more visual, with the operations actually written beside or inside the symbols. (See below) These are very good for brainstorming, group discussions, presentations and so on. Make sure though that the Flow Sheet is attached or referenced somewhere on this larger diagram, along with location, system, process, date and all of the other information that you would find at the top of the flow sheets.

However, the main advantage of this larger diagram is obvious when the two large 'Ideal' and 'Actual' diagrams are side by side (and hopefully to a similar scale for ease of comparison). It will be much easier to see where the deviations occur. I suggest the use of plotter paper for this, as it will be about 1metre wide and 100metres long. Plenty of room for the most complicated of diagrams.

And this is where the fun really begins, the actual steps involved in solving the problem.

Hints on completion of the Sheets

- The Process Flow Sheet should flow, that is to say there should be no ambiguities in the recording of it, no jumping from one section to another and then returning to yet another.
- It is important that the information gathered here is accurate, both for a general overview and more so for problem solving.

- Ensure that all the information asked for on the chart is completed, location, date, time etc. This will help future reference.
- Comparing Ideal and Actual will highlight potential problem areas.
- Keep a record of suggestions for change.
- Keep a record of potential problem areas.

Let's have a look at a larger, symbol-focused sheet. This is a small section from the System Flow Sheet for Shopping:

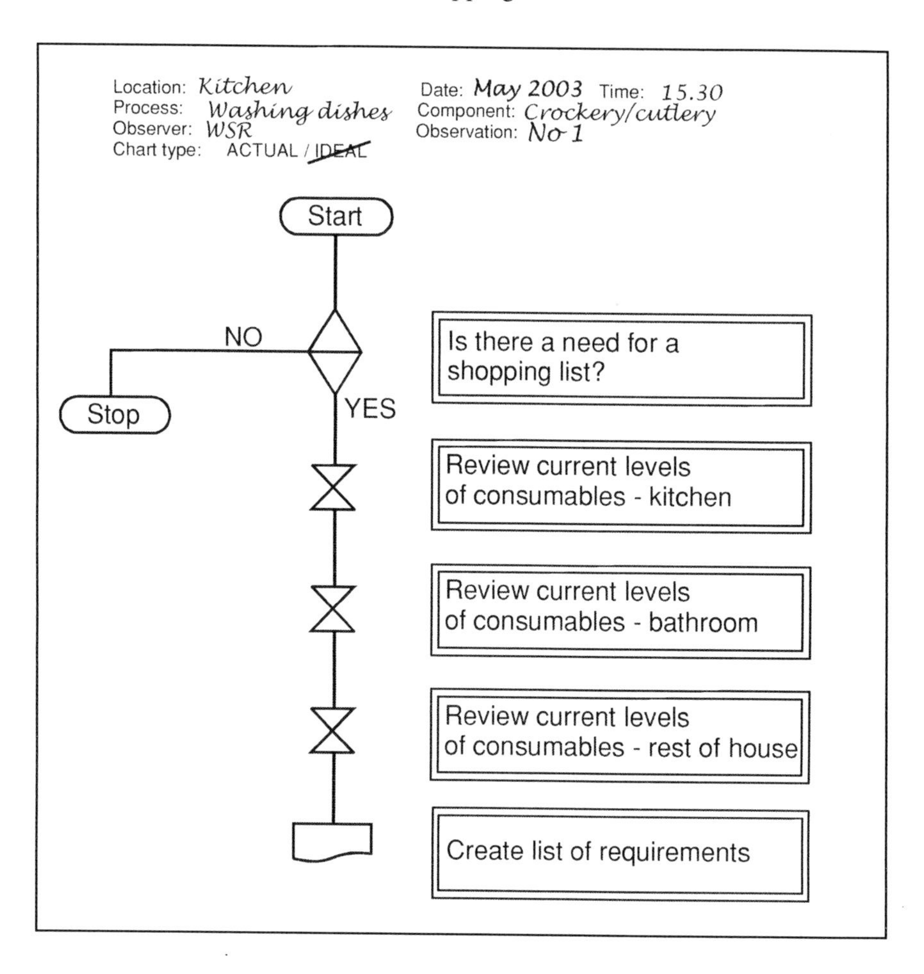

The Jobs Themselves

What Is 5S?

5S is merely a set of simple instructions that lead to a clean, safe and efficient work area. As the name suggests, 5S refers to five things beginning with the letter 'S' that lead to this. Rumour has it that 5S did not come out of the automotive industry, or any other industry for that matter, but was the process that Japanese housewives followed when they were doing their spring cleaning. Possibly.

A lot of visiting, experienced kaizen experts or consultants will not even entertain the possibility of carrying out any work within a factory or office unless there is a well established 5S program in place. Even then, they will be critical and usually try to incorporate an additional 5S event into the main event.

5S is looked upon as being the backbone of the entire kaizen and lean production philosophy.

5S is the means to an end, the end being a long-term minimisation of non-value-adding cleaning work and effort and improving the overall appearance of the company. 5S increases the company's productivity. 5S makes the workplace safer. 5S makes the company look good. 5S makes the company more efficient.

So, what are the five Ss? (and the Japanese equivalents)

1st S – Simplify (Seiri) Use only the bare minimum of equipment. If you are in doubt about anything, then throw it out.

2nd S – Straighten (Seiton) A place for everything and everything in its place.

3rd S – Scrub (Seiso) Remove all traces of dirt and grime. All traces.

4th S – Stabilise (Seiketsu) Make improvements to ensure that the area stays in the clean condition you now find it in.

5th S – Sustain (Shitsuke) Benchmark. Regulate. Take pride.

The Most Important 5S Fact

5S will work most efficiently when we start with the 1st S and work our way systematically to the 5th S.

There is no point trying to scrub an area if it is littered with unwanted tools and paperwork, if it has not been simplified. There is no point trying to sustain a level of cleanliness if the area has not been stabilised.

How is it Implemented?

An area of the workplace is chosen to be put through the 5S experience. This may be a production area, the sales office or the managing director's desk. 5S is relevant to all areas.

Once the area is chosen, a second holding area must be clearly marked out to house all the items in the 5S area that are not bolted down.

After this, take a video or a series of pictures of the area in order to obtain a before and after comparison. The team will then go through the following steps:

1st S – Simplify

The team members each take control of a section of the work area and remove everything that is not bolted down. We mean *everything*.

Spanners, Allen keys, paperwork, kettles, paper punches, wrenches, desks, tables, tool cabinets, staplers – *everything*.

These are all placed in the holding area. The main area of the event has now been simplified.

Items to consider

The following lists identify items that should be looked at critically, and the question asked 'Do we need them?'

Production Areas	***Office Areas***
Cabinets	Books
Cleaning Equipment	Cabinets
Components	Catalogues
Documents	Magazines
Gauges	Paper
Machinery	Records
Packaging	Samples
Parts	Shelving
Tables	Stationary
Tooling	Supplies

2nd S – Straighten

'A place for everything and everything in its place' best sums up this section. As I mentioned, 5S was developed by housewives as part of the spring cleaning. And we all have a small 5S area around our houses, more than one probably, but we don't realise it. If you go into the kitchen and look for a fork, chances are it will be in a drawer near the sink, and segregated from the knives, spoons and tea spoons with the use of a small plastic tray. Odds on that you will store all of your towels in the same cupboard, probably the same cupboard that the hot water tank is in. Point is, you know where something is when you need it. Why then do we leave cheque books in a different place every time we put them down, and spend a great deal of time looking for car keys?

Decide what is needed and what is not needed.

Each person gathers a handful of tools and returns to their machine, cabinet, desk, whatever and replaces the bare minimum.

For instance all hexagonal socket screws have the appropriate Allen key inserted, all nuts and bolts have the appropriate spanner placed on them.

However this doesn't mean that if there are ten hexagonal socket screws then ten Allen keys are required. One key can be used for all of these screws if it is placed in the correct position.

Every factory, and indeed every location within a factory, has a secret area for tools. By this we mean a box that is full of old and worn Allen keys, bastard spanners, adjustable wrenches, pens, shim and a whole host of tools that are so old that nobody knows what they are. Most of them are of no use to anyone. However, those that are of use take an age to find because of the others.

If equipment is surplus to requirements, then do not keep it. We don't get emotional over spanners.

Through the use of Straightening, only the *essentials* are in the area.

Remember – **If in doubt, throw it out**.

Remember also though – by 'throw it out' we mean remove it from the section under consideration. If another area of the workplace requires a piece of equipment, then let them have it. This may seem to run in the face of what we are trying to do by merely moving equipment from one area to another, but if they have been through the 5S process previously, then the system will allow this extra piece of equipment to be incorporated in the correct manner. If they haven't carried out 5S before, then the equipment may be removed when they do carry 5S out.

Additionally, if there is a piece of expensive equipment that is no longer required, then you may decide to either sell it or store it for future use. You would not consider throwing it into the skip.

A, B and C space

'A' space is the area around the operators, the area they can reach without having to move away, the area where they spend most of their time when working on machinery.

Everything in this area is essential. Everything in this area is used daily. Quality gauges and paperwork are a good example.

'B' space is the area around the machinery, where tools used weekly are stored. Items that are not essential to the daily running. Tools for unusual situations.

Everything in this area is essential, but it is not used daily.

'C' space is the area where we keep the non-essential items. The area where items that are used perhaps once a year are kept – sealant, glue, hydraulic jacks, ball races, cutting tools.

This is more commonly known as 'The Storeroom.'

A little drawing:

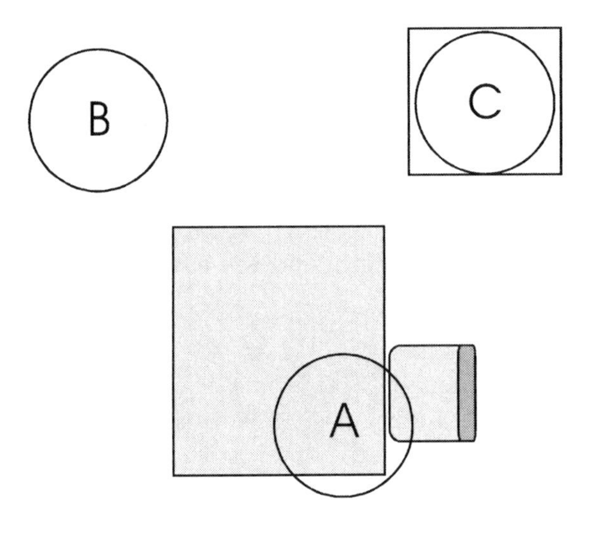

One of the most advantageous tools to use in the setting up of the Straighten stage is the use of Shadow Boards. A board is placed within the work area, that accommodates all of the tools required. All of the tools are then placed on this board and a line is drawn around them. The area within the line is then coloured in order to provide a silhouette and a contrast. (Yellow lines/colouring on a black background for instance).

These need not be specially built boards. Any surface on the machine itself can be used, however you should try to use a vertical surface rather than a horizontal one. If you use a horizontal surface you will realise that it will be more difficult to keep clean.

And how do we decide where these boards go?

Ask the operator where they want them. They will be a part of the team, but in this instance there will be less emphasis on a team decision. Also ask the other operators who work in this area. Some aspects may change from operator to operator, such as being left- or right-handed.

Ensure the operator doesn't have to stretch or turn. People for years have always laughed at the stereotypical view of those working for Japanese firms as coming to work in the morning and having to do their daily exercises. Ha, ha, ha! If you play any form of sport, you will always warm up. Stretching exercises for football, rugby, golf, a few pints of beer for darts, a couple of games beforehand for snooker. But you are perfectly willing to fall out of bed, drive to work and start working straight away. This is potentially very damaging to the body, especially if there is lifting of any sort involved. So avoid stretching and turning.

Watch where operators place tools after use. That's where they want the tools to be. And if you look closely, you will notice that they don't even look when they put the tools down, they know instinctively where they go.

Using shadow boards lets the operator know two things:

1. where the tools are always located (a simple form of standardisation)
2. if there are any tools missing.

After use for a short time, the operator will be able to pick up tools without having to look for them.

An even better situation

As mentioned, if there are ten hexagonal socket screws, you don't need ten

Allen keys. One will do for all of them, if they are within easy reach. (You obviously don't want the operators having to carry tools about with them.)

Another option is to weld Allen keys in place so as to reduce time spent picking them up, placing them in the socket and replacing them on a board. This is particularly useful when there are a number of different sizes of Allen keys involved.

However, this should be treated with caution and a bit of thought. If the key has to be placed on a moving section of the machine, then it may catch the operator or interfere with other parts of the machine.

If this proves impractical or there are too many different keys to work with easily, then try to ensure that the sockets are all of a uniform size. This may involve spark eroding to a standard size or redesigning aspects of the machine itself, but in the long run it will be worth it.

A major manufacturer of socket screws took this approach. However, they found it reasonably easy as all they had to do was change the socket forming punch at the end of a run to the required size and produce a couple of dozen more.

Consider also

Storage methods	Easy access, in clearly laid out locations for tooling and tools.
Clearly marked locations	Let people know what is where.
Signs	Identify the area. Let others know what is produced there.

Remember the following

- If there is a flat surface or a box, it will very quickly fill up with unwanted items. (The smaller the area, the more people try and squeeze into it.)
- No stretching. No turning.
- Ask the operator what they want, and where they want it.
- A place for everything. Everything in its place.

3rd S – Scrub

As you would expect, this is the part of the exercise where the cleaning gets done. Every surface is scrubbed clean of not just dust and grime but oil, grease, loose paint, coffee stains. We mean:

Every surface – scrubbed clean.

Nice, big letters. Very important.

This is the part of the 5S process that results in a presentable face that can be shown without fear to customers.

If the exercise is carried out in a production area, the floor must be completely washed. All oil puddles mopped up. Sumps cleaned out. Loose components removed from under machines.

While this is being carried out, the team should be looking for the reasons behind the dirt. As they mop up the oil, they should be looking for the source. As they pick up the loose components, they should be looking for the gaps and holes in the chutes or transfer systems. Ask:

- Why is there oil on the floor?
- Where did all of these components come from?
- Why are the light shades three inches thick with dust?

And this is the start of the introduction of the 5 Whys into the 5S section. Read once again the section in the Tool Box as a refresher. The 5 Whys will be put to use in Section 4, Stabilise.

Some companies like to take the opportunity here to repaint floors, machinery, tables and the like in order to create a 'cleaner' workplace. This is at the company's discretion. However, it makes the area very visible and this allows those not participating in the exercise to see the changes a bit more clearly.

It is also a bit more professional-looking.

4th S – Stabilise

Improvements are essential if the area is to remain in the clean condition that you now find it in.

The 3rd S is traditionally the worst part due to the fact that most areas never see a brush or cloth. A lot of work and effort goes into it. We don't want to do that every week.

So what do we do? We **stabilise**.

This is the main reason for 5 Whys – If there is oil on the floor, where has it come from? Find the leak. Repair it.

If components are scattered around, how did they get there?

Increase the efficiency of chutes and hoppers. Completely cover them if necessary. Use clear Perspex if viewing is required.

Why do we have five year old paperwork in the office?

Check if it is needed. If it is, store somewhere else. In the basement for instance. Most companies keep 18 months worth of paperwork. Check your legal requirements and company procedures.

If a machine broke down with the same problem every month, maintenance would soon find the problem and solve it at its simplest level. Do the same with the 4th S. Okay, so maybe the maintenance department wouldn't do this and just plod along, but that is no excuse for you to do likewise.

Make the best use of the 5 Whys. Identify the source. Solve it.

As part of the 2nd section, Straighten, each item of equipment should be in the position that provides the best working conditions, a place for everything and everything in its place. How do we know if it is where it should be? All machinery, tables, cabinets etc. should have their location clearly marked out, whether on the floor, the wall or hanging from the ceiling. This can be done simply by painting right-angles around the corners of the item, printing signs up, using self-stick labels, whatever. The contents of cabinets should also be detailed, though not in too much detail. You may for instance write 'Quality Paperwork' on the front of the cabinet rather than detail all of the individual sheets used.

This is another section that some people laugh at. The 'stupid label' section where everything has its name placed on it. It will provide long-term benefits, so don't worry.

A friend of mine was coming up for retirement. He was a kaizen specialist and a very active person. His wife joked that she was dreading having him around the house. (Maybe it wasn't a joke.) She said that she fully expected the kettle to have 'Kettle' written on it after a week and a large yellow circle painted on their kitchen worktop.

If machinery is moved in and out of the work area occasionally, then the location of this machinery should also be marked out on the floor along with its name or serial number.

These items should also have some form of locating device fitted to ensure accuracy. There is no point in correcting the location of chutes and the like if the machine itself is out of position. One commonly used locating device is the sliding bolts used on gates, fitted vertically to locate into specially drilled holes in the floor. Much easier than messing around with catches and rawl-bolts.

The 4th S can be summed up in the following manner:

Make It So It Cannot Happen

5th S – Sustain

It should be obvious what this section is designed to do.

Write up a daily, weekly and monthly procedures list, detailing actions that the operators have to follow, such as washing the floor, wiping general dust off of the surfaces, checking for leaks. Each list should be designed to last for a week or a month, and signed off after each set of procedures is completed. (See example on page 64)

Further Ideas

- A Janitor Station is mentioned in the sheet. This is an area where brushes, mops, shovels, paper towels etc. can be stored for general use. Use the principles of silhouette lines or a list to show what should and should not be there.
- Benchmark. The pictures and video that you may have taken at the start of the exercise will allow you to benchmark against yourself. Other areas should be looking to benchmark against you.
- Regulate. Introduce a check sheet to continually monitor the area and provide feedback.
- Always practice 1st S through to 4th S.
- Take pride. Let the operators be responsible for their work area. Create ownership. (This may provide you with some trouble if there is a shift system operating, due to one operator not pulling his weight, but are you going to let one person stand in the way of Lean Production?)
- Make it a part of the working day. Turn the procedures into a way of life.
- Achieve the discipline.

5S Procedures List

Location:
Week commencing Monday ________________ 200   Sheet signed off by unit manager ____________________________

PROCEDURES	Monday			Tuesday			Wednesday			Thursday			Friday		
To be carried out every shift	D	B	N	D	B	N	D	B	N	D	B	N	D	B	N
Check for oil leaks															
Check for water leaks															
Check all tooling in place															
Check the chutes for damage															
To be carried out once per day															
Sweep the floor															
Check the lights for faults															
Check wash plant for damage															
Check janitor station is correctly stocked															
To be carried out weekly															
Wipe machine surfaces clean															
Check floor for damage/dirt build-up															
Check surroundings for concerns															

Please initial the clear boxes that correspond with your shift.
If there are concerns with the section, please raise them immediately with the area charge hand

Additional comments:

If the work area is in the same condition six months from now as it was when the exercise ended, then you know that the exercise was a success.

If the work area is in the same condition six months from now as it was when the exercise started, then you have not only wasted time and effort, you are not serious about making improvements.

Monitoring

Once the exercise has been completed, a form of monitoring is required, such as a 5S Patrol Sheet, designed to provide a weekly, fortnightly or monthly check on the area. The frequency of the patrols should decrease as the time period from the event increases. For instance, you may carry out a patrol initially every week for a month, then once a fortnight for a month and finally on a monthly basis. This helps to ensure that the good work achieved in the event stays at a high level in the immediate aftermath, the most crucial period.

These sheets, although generic in nature, are specific to a certain area or group of similar areas. (You would not consider the use of the same check sheet for the warehouse that you would use for the foundry.) Notice though that this Patrol Sheet is different from the Procedures List that you introduced. One provides information on what has to be done, the other monitors.

The Patrol should ideally consist of two people, each of whom gives a mark to a given aspect, independently of the other. The marks are then compared and if different, discussed to bring them into line with each other or given an average.

The Patrol Team give a mark of 1 to 5 for each Subject, and the higher the Total Count, the better the area has done. Obviously then, 1 is poor, 5 is good.

If a Subject scores 3 or less, then the item has failed. In the event of this, the item is noted in the 5S Register as having failed. (A copy of this can be seen further on.)

At the Kaizen Review meetings that you will hold (on a regular basis), these sheets can be presented to form the feedback required for the group to monitor the continued success. In the early months, I would present all patrol sheets. However, as the systems develop and increase, only areas that fail badly should be presented. These failures will be the exceptions to the rule.

A Patrol Sheet can be seen on the following pages. This Patrol Sheet is designed around a foundry area.

The 'Patrol Number' is merely a reference number for traceability in the future. These numbers should be kept in a separate record, with a note of the area concerned, date, time, who carried out the patrol, and the final percentage.

The Patrol Sheet is easily completed, with total scores and percentages calculated. The advantage of percentages is that if the sheet changes, there is some form of continuation, and the percentages can also be used to track improvements visually on a graph.

As mentioned, any subject scoring a 3 or less is regarded as having failed. If it fails, it should be repaired. And if it is going to be repaired, who is going to repair it? Not the team who were involved in the event in the first instance, but the person who is responsible for the area. After all, if they are running the area on a day-to-day basis, why should a team come in to clean up their mess?

To keep a track of the work needing done, we use a 5S Register. The registers form a record of all 5S Patrols. Once the register has been completed, it is the responsibility of the person in charge of the area to ensure that it is up to date, and that all departments or people responsible for correcting any faults are informed. (Remember the part about Ownership? This applies to Management as well.) As such, this person will liaise with the departments involved and appoint trustees.

'Sheet Number' refers to the number of the sheet showing the failures. (1 of 2, 2 of 2) 'Comments' can be added by anyone as further reference or information.

Once completed, a copy of the register and the patrol sheet is given to the person in charge of the area concerned, and a copy displayed in the area, with the register usually on a red background to highlight it. The fact that it is displayed in the area helps to ensure that the actions are completed.

The actions should aim to be completed within one week.

As you will see, the register is a mixture of information, requests and recommendations. Due to the fact that we are dealing empirically with a range of marks, there are no real yes or no answers, so there has to be a bit of give and take. We could create a Patrol Sheet that asked extremely specific questions (Is there a glove bin in the area, is it full to a reasonable level, is the lid closed and is it yellow?), but this would be cumbersome and people would lose interest. And what would you specify as a 'reasonable level' or to what shade of yellow would you go before it became cream?

A 5S Register is shown on page 68.

5S Patrol Sheet

Patrol no: *291*
Location: *Foundry 1 - m/c5* Observer: *WSR* Total count: *99/150*
Date: *Xx/xx/2003* Time: *13-05* Percentage: *62%*

	SUBJECT	ITEMS TO BE CHECKED	Poor ←→ Good				
			1	2	3	4	5
1	1. Floor	Is it clean?				●	
2		Is it litter free?			●		
3		Is there oil on the floor?				●	
4		Is there water on the floor?				●	
5		Are there castings on the floor?		●			
6		Is there flash on the floor?	●				
7		Is there piping lying about?		●			
8		Is the pit free from rubbish?	●				
9		Is the gully free from rubbish?	●				
10		Is there a rubbish bin in the area?				●	
11		Are registers and packers in designated areas?					●
12	2. Machine	Is there oil/grease on any non-moving parts?		●			
13		Is there water on the machine?		●			
14		Is there aluminium build-up on the shot end?	●				
15		Is there aluminium build-up on bumper bars?	●				
16		Are all tools/tooling in designated areas?				●	
17	3. Furnace	Is there aluminium build-up anywhere?	●				
18		Is it clean?			●		
19		Is it litter free?			●		
20	4. Robot	Is it covered?		●			
21		Is the cover clean?			●		
22		Is the gully covered in this area?	●				
23	5. Visual Comms	Area name clearly displayed?					●
24		Component names clearly displayed?					●
25		Cell layout plan present and up-to-date?					●
26		Operator names and pictures displayed?					●
27		5S information shown?					●
28		Fire point information shown?					●
29	6. General	Is there a warm-up bin in the general area?				●	
30		Is janitor station fully stocked?					●
31		Is there unrequired tooling in the area?			●		
32		Is there a glove bin in the general area?			●		
33							
34							
35							

1. Simplify 2. Straighten 3. Scrub 4. Stabilise 5. Sustain

5S Register

Patrol no: Sheet No:
Location: Date:

Item	Failures - corrective action	Trustee	Comments
2	Ensure cleaning is included in the Procedures List and adhered to	DG	
	Provide additional time and equipment if required		
5	Not enough scrap casting bins provided	CS	
	Operators not adhering to 5S procedures		
6	Review dies for venting	T room	Toolroom should review closing gap
	Fit guards to the casting area to contain flash and machine pit		
7	Ensure that all piping is returned to the toolroom with the removed dies	DG	Include on Changeover Check Sheet
8	Provide time and equipment to clear the machine pit daily	DG	
	Review the contents of the pit and eliminate rubbish production		
9	Cover the gully over	Maint	Item 2 will help with this situation. Rubbish in the gully can lead to filter blockage. V Important
12	Maintenance to review current greasing methods	Maint	
	Oil sump at rear is leaking - Drain and repair		
13	Leak from die lubrication system. Replace worn nozzles and correct spray area of all nozzles	Maint	
14	Review clearance between the bush and the register to eliminate aluminium spraying	T room	Drawing office
15	Replace worn/damaged collets on fixed die	T room	Toolroom at next changeover
17	Fit a lip to the furnace opening	Maint	
18	As item 2	DG	
19	Provide rubbish bin and ensure that it is used	DG	
20	Replace with new cover	Maint	The cover is badly damaged through aluminium splash, is torn and doesn't cover entire robot
21	As item 2	DG	
22	Cover the gully over, as item 9	Maint	
31	Remove unwanted/unrequired tooling	T room	Toolroom to fabricate new racks
32	There is a bin, however it is full to overflowing. Ensure that it is emptied on a regular basis	DG	

It may seem that there is a lot of paperwork in this section, however most of it is designed to ensure that the work and effort carried out in the initial exercise is kept moving along. If things are going to fail, it will be in the first few weeks following the event.

Secondly, the paperwork acts as a monitor of the system, so as well as being a catalyst to keep the momentum going, if things do start to slip, there is a quick and very visual record of the failings as they occur. It is then up to management to get things moving again.

This does not mean shouting at people – as with all aspects of Lean Production, find out the reasons.

The paperwork can be reduced and eventually eliminated over time as the workforce develops a greater understanding of the systems. In the meantime I cannot stress enough the importance of 5S, and due to this it must be completed correctly, maintained and allowed to spread to other sections. The paperwork is essential in the short term.

To Recap

1st S	**Simplify**
2nd S	**Straighten**
3rd S	**Scrub**
4th S	**Stabilise**
5th S	**Sustain**

Benefits – 1st S through to 5th S

- Less Waste
- Greater Safety
- Easier Maintenance
- Improved Quality
- Creates Pride and Respect
- Develops a Positive Attitude

Make 5S a way of life. You already practise it in the home, so apply it at work.

TPM – Total Productive Maintenance

Through the use of a TPM system, we aim to reduce the amount of time lost to production due to maintenance issues. Basically, we are aiming to eliminate breakdowns by fixing problems before they occur. And we aim to succeed in this by doing a little bit of maintenance when it is convenient rather than a lot when it isn't.

Sometimes it is also called Total Preventative Maintenance – however the 'Productive' covers Preventative, Reactive (what you do when a breakdown does occur), and Predictive (the use of analysis, vibration detection, condition monitoring etc.) Maintenance.

We will be covering all of these areas. You may ask 'why will we consider Reactive maintenance if we are eliminating breakdowns?'. There are non-value added checks to consider – checks that take longer to perform than it would take to fix a problem. For instance, checks may require the machine to be stopped where the stop-start sequence takes longer than the repair.

Some aspects of Predictive tend to be implemented through bespoke and specialist use of equipment, where all that you really have to do in the main is wait for the machine to tell you that something is going to go wrong. (In the day-to-day use of TPM, most predictive maintenance makes good use of electronic indicators.)

Have a look at the following drawing.

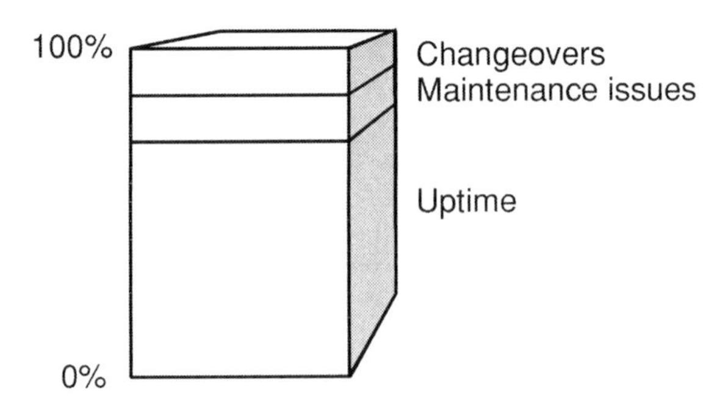

This is a typical, if slightly exaggerated, representation of the working day on a piece of plant in a factory. In heavier industries, there may also be a lot of time lost through issues concerning dies and the like, but in the main there are only really three areas. The issues concerning dies should be addressed through a specialised maintenance program, the basis of which will be formed by TPM.

The point is that if there is maintenance being carried out, it is generally being done in time that should be used for production. (Likewise for SMED, the following section). You will find that, unless there is a comprehensive TPM scheme in place, maintenance will only be carried out when the machine has broken down.

Through the use of TPM, we should be aiming for a working hour split that looks like the following:

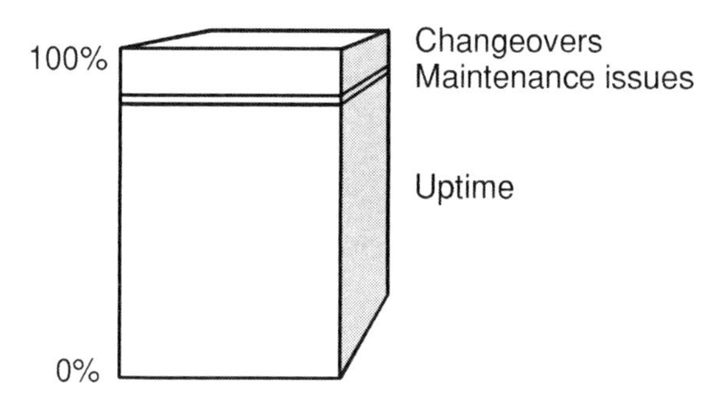

As can be seen, the ideal situation would be one of maximum uptime with minimum downtime due to maintenance issues – with the changeovers being addressed later.

The main advantages

If our machines are running for a greater percentage of the available time, then:

- The company can make better use of and protect its capital plant.
  'Better use of' is another way of saying 'running for a greater amount of time', and obviously the less the machine is stood waiting to be repaired the better. The protection of the plant comes through the elimination of catastrophic failure. (Without TPM, depending on the size of the failure you may be better off sticking the machine on the back of a lorry and taking it to the scrap yard.)
- You can produce cheaper components.
  The greater the uptime, the greater the production. When the machine is

standing you are still paying operator wages, you are paying maintenance fitters and overheads.

- Less overtime will have to be worked.
  As above, the greater the uptime, the greater the production, therefore the greater the production per shift then the fewer shifts you have to run for. (Or part shifts). Remember the CPE analysis?
- Less stock will be held.
  If you are confident in the production capabilities of your plant then you can start to reduce the safety level of stock that you hold. If you think that you may have a weeks major breakdown once a year then you will want to hold a weeks stock in order to ensure customer supply.

The risk of large scale failure is reduced if you have a fair idea that it is about to happen, therefore spare parts and urgent replacements do not have to be purchased at a moment's notice, with special delivery and the like.

If you are confident about your TPM system, then you can drastically reduce your spare part stock, possibly to zero. For example, by knowing that you will require a component in January for machine 1, in February for machine 2 and so on, you order as and when required, as opposed to possibly holding six in stock all the time. You may hold none in stock and require your parts supplier to hold one in stock for you at all times to ensure immediate delivery in the event of an unforeseen breakdown. (They do occur).

So, how do we start tackling the maintenance side of things?

First off, it is important to be fully aware of the following – TPM is not purely a maintenance department concern. There are two clear situations, operator TPM checks and maintenance TPM checks. Operator checks tend to be more frequent, say daily, whilst maintenance checks tend to be longer term, monthly or quarterly. A split like this, coupled with a reduction in breakdown issues, allows the time-served, skilled and trained members of the maintenance department the freedom to carry out much more valuable tasks, such as project support, new product development and additional continuous improvement work.

I said earlier that we are aiming to fix the problem before it occurs. That is the whole premise of TPM. In order to do this we must ask ourselves one vital question:

What is the minimum time required between checks?

The secret of TPM can best be describes as this – What is the time scale between the initiation of a problem and a catastrophic failure? For instance, if you had a drip from a lubrication system, how long would it take for the oil level to reach a stage where it was no longer capable of performing? Or, if the machine will run for four hours without any lubrication, then obviously it would be prudent to check every 3 hours and 59 minutes that it is being lubricated. If you checked every 4 hours one minute, then you run the risk of ruining the machine. So, all of our checks have to be brought into the time window that the specific piece of the equipment allows.

How to start the system off

There are a number of clear steps that should be followed, and, bearing in mind that TPM should be implemented as any other project would be, it should have controls like any other project.

1. Identify the need for TPM
2. Select the project team
3. Identify the checks required
4. Identify the specifics of each check
5. Brief the workplace
6. Run out TPM in a trial area
7. Implement across the factory
8. Monitor

NOTE – Items 1, 2, 5, 6, 7 and 8 can be applied to all shopfloor-based project work.

1. Identify the need for TPM

We have already shown the advantages of TPM through the diagrams above, and to be honest, if I have to tell you that it is always a good idea to reduce the amount of downtime, then you are in the wrong job. However, make sure that TPM is the best place in which to use your limited resources.

This may sound rather obvious, but if you remember from the 'Tools' section, there is no room for the use of 'gut-feelings'. Too many people get what they think of as a bright idea and rush headlong into it without any thought. However, a bit of analysis will not go amiss. (Refer to the section on Pareto for information about gathering and analysing data). If you do not have any major breakdown issues, but take fourteen hours to change between product runs, then consider SMED first.

If it is felt that TPM should be carried out at this moment in time, then consider the following.

a. Target the areas where the greatest benefits can be obtained.
b. Pick areas where an early success story is guaranteed – it will make it easier when you go into the difficult areas.

2. Select the project team

This will be the single most important aspect of the TPM project, as it will save vast amounts of time in the future and make the whole process easier when running out on the shop floor.

The make up of the team should depend on the type of machinery involved, obviously. However, the last TPM system that I worked on had a team comprising shift electrician, process improvements manager, production manager, operators, facilitator, shift fitter, area manager and the head of the maintenance department and his deputy. The company Production Director oversaw the whole project as mentor.

A bit excessive you might think, but the machinery was very large and complex, with over 40 individual pieces of plant involved. The make up of the team was selected mainly because of the experience of the actual maintenance crews. Managers were there to lend a bit of clout and allocate resources as required, but also to gain an understanding of the TPM project. The facilitator was required to not only do all of the running around, printing sheets, purchasing of materials as and when required, information gathering and the like, but to act as the monitor of the system once it was in place. Process Improvements were represented to ensure that there was no conflict between this project and others that were running, as well as managing the whole project.

And the Production Director was there to make sure that everything was actually carried out.

Pick your team carefully. As can be seen, the involvement of senior people is essential, as a bit of clout will undoubtedly be needed. Do not take people who can be spared because there is nothing else for them to do. Experience and understanding of the systems and machinery involved are the main criteria, so pick the most appropriate maintenance people that there are. Operators are always an essential part, as they will highlight day-to-day problems or aspects that no one else will have considered.

The involvement of an operator will also make it easier to sell the project to the shop floor, as they have had a voice in the decision making process. Likewise the involvement of electricians and fitters.

Depending on the time scales involved, the team should decide what amount of time is required from them. Again, on the last TPM I was involved with, the team met for 1½ hours a day for eight weeks. (This generally lasted for 2 to 2½ hours daily.) As with everything else, if this is the first time that you have done it, you will be flying by the seat of your pants, so try and be flexible, but I can say now that no matter what time you set aside, you will wish that you had more.

3. Identify the checks required

You may want to refer to the '5Why' section for a refresher, as it should be put to good use here as part of the analysing.

So, identify the checks. This is not as easy as it may sound. Yes, initially it is easy to say what should be checked, but after that, you will start to delve deeper and deeper into all of the possibilities. I will try and take you through step by step :-

a) If possible, split the machinery up into distinct sections. For instance, if you were dealing with your car, you might want to segregate the following: engine, tyres, lights, windows, internal fittings, bodywork, peripherals.
b) Decide what aspects of this machinery can stop production and/or create poor working conditions. There are a number of sources for this information – previous initiatives, common sense, manufacturers' recommendations, historical information, recent information gathering initiatives, all of which when brought together will provide a huge amount of potential checks.
c) The common sense part requires the team to actually discuss the situations that may occur, and talk through the information already in front of them with a view to adding any additional checks that experience tells them are required.

Master Reference Table

All of this information should be plotted as the team progresses, the best way of doing this through the use of a spreadsheet. (If possible, try and put together an overhead projection from a lap-top or PC). It should be split into distinct sections, as the information is, and will include the following:

Reference	A number that will stay with that check
What to check for	Engine, tyres, lights, windows, oil, water, leaks etc.
How to check	Where and/or how to actually perform the check – light on main control panel, visual water level check, thermometer check.
Conditions to meet	The specified operating parameters that the result must fall into – a temperature range, either on or off, all safety guards fitted, no leaks.
Action if failed	What to do in the event that the condition is not met – inform engineering, repair yourself, stop machine and inform supervisor.
Frequency of check	How often the check is carried out.
Responsibility	Who will actually carry out the check.
Decision	Who was present at the meeting when this check was decided upon. This will allow feedback in the future if there are any queries.

These in turn will be split up into the various sub-sections of the plant, be they engine, tyres, lights and so on.

The Master Reference table may look like the page opposite:

Explanation

The first pieces of information input onto the Master Reference Table will be the actual checks themselves, and I suggest that the team carries on with this aspect rather than trying to complete the entire set of information for each check as it comes along. The reason being that, in the next stages of the project, we will be aiming to reduce the amount of checks and so any additional work carried out here will possibly be wasted.

It is important that after every meeting this spreadsheet is updated with the new information that has been provided, and a hard copy made available at the next meeting for reference purposes. If you have access to a plotter (from a CAD station perhaps) then make good use of it. The hard copy should be of a reasonably large size so that everyone in the team can read it without any problems. Remember, there may be ten of you around a table, so the clearer and larger the better.

Master Reference Table

Team members - AA, BB, CC, DD, EE, FF, GG

Project uptime

Ref	What to check for	How to check	Condition to meet	Action if failed	Freq	Resp	Decision
	Engine checks						
1	Oil level	Use dip stick	Within dipstick parameters	Fill/drain until within parameters	D	Driver	BB CC DD EE FF
2	Water level	Visual	Reaches level on water container	Fill to level immediately	D	Driver	BB CC DD EE FF
3	Fan belt tension	Touch	Movement less than 1"	Tighten	M	Mech	BB CC DD EE FF
	Tyre checks						
4	Pressure	Use pressure guage	Within 28-30 psi	Inflate/deflate to parameters	W	Driver	BB CC EE FF
5	Tread thickness	Use tread guage	Within legal requirements	Replace immediately	W	Driver	BB CC EE FF
6	Wear	Visual	No flat areas in central section	Replace immediately	W	Driver	AA BB CC DD EE FF
7	Damage	Visual	No foreign bodies or ripped	Replace immediately	W	Driver	AA BB CC DD EE FF
	Light checks						
8	Clean	Visual	No build-up of dirt on glass	Clean	D	Driver	AA BB CC DD EE FF
9	Working	Visual	Bulbs work when switched on	Replace broken bulbs	D	Driver	AA BB CC DD EE FF
10	Light glass not chipped	Visual	Glass is free from damage	Replace light housing	W	Mech	AA BB CC DD EE FF
	Window checks						
11	Present	Visual	All windows are fitted	See windscreen specialist	O	Driver	AA BB CC DD EE FF
12	Window glass not chipped	Visual	No damage to the glass	Replace/repair	W	Mech	AA BB CC DD EE FF
13	Sealed correctly	Visual	Water does not leak into car	See windscreen specialist	M	Mech	AA BB CC DD EE FF
	Internal fitting checks						
14	Clean	Visual and touch	No dust/dirt on fittings	Clean interior	W	Driver	AA BB CC DD FF
15	Aesthetically good	Visual	Fitted correctly and no damage	Replace/repair	O	Driver	AA DD EE FF
16	Window winder works	Operate	Windows move up and down	Repair	O	Driver	AA DD EE FF
	Bodywork checks						
17	Bodywork free from dents	Visual	No dents in bodywork	Assess damage - ignore/replace/repair	W	Mech	AA CC DD EE FF
18	Rust	Visual	No rust in bodywork	Repair damaged areas	M	Mech	AA CC DD EE FF
	Peripheral checks						
19	Mirrors in good condition	Visual	Mirrors present and undamaged	Assess damage - ignore/replace/repair	O	Driver	AA BB DD EE FF
20	Arial	Visual and operation	Present and receiving FM	Replace/repair or check connections	O	Driver	AA BB DD EE FF
21	Tow bar	Visual	Present and connected correctly	Replace or refit correctly	M	Mech	AA BB CC DD EE FF

Once this has been carried out, you are likely to have a huge list, split into distinct sections, and you may find this slightly daunting. Nevertheless with a bit more discussion, you will quickly find that a lot of the checks can be eliminated :-

a. Remove non-value adding checks. These are described as checks that take longer to carry out than it would take to repair the machinery if it failed. Common sense.
b. Review the checks again and try to incorporate some with others. A basic statement, but if there are a hundred possible checks already on your sheet, then some will undoubtedly be very similar. 'X' may be the result of 'Y', therefore if the 'Y' is checked, is there any need to check 'X'?
c. Can manual tasks be automated? In your car, you have a dip-stick to check the oil level, but this is designed to tell you how much oil you should put in once the level has dropped, as all modern cars have real-time electronic oil level detection systems. The dip stick is not there for you to check before every journey, or once a week/month/year whatever. The electronics replace the need to check, but once the problem has been flagged, the dip stick acts as a manual guide allowing you to re-fill to the correct level indicated. This electronic system is Predictive maintenance.

If you want to check the water temperature of your car engine, you would not stop every 10 miles, lift the bonnet, remove the cap from the water sump and insert a thermometer. No. You have a built-in thermometer that constantly carries out real-time monitoring, and when the temperature is greater than the engine specification, a light will illuminate on your dashboard or a gauge will show you. Simple engineering, with no skill other than sight involved, and if unfortunately you cannot see, then you shouldn't be driving. (What else happened here? We went from preventive maintenance to predictive maintenance.)

As part of the overall discussions, engineering possibilities such as this should be considered, for the reason described above.

The first two steps, a. and b., may reduce the number of checks drastically whilst the last step will reduce the amount of time required to carry out the checks.

What you are left with is a series of checks, split up into distinct sections. (Engines, tyres, lights etc.) Each check should now have a distinct reference number, this number to stay with that check for ever more. The reason for this is that, as the checks are split up into the various sheets (weekly engineering, monthly electrical etc.), there is always a reference from these sheets to the Master Reference Table.

4. Identify the specifics of each check

You should now have a short-list of checks, (which may be rather long.) You have identified the 'What' but must now concentrate on the 'When', 'Who' and 'How'.

The 'When' aspect we have already touched upon –

When is the minimum time required between checks?

Once again, this information comes from a combination of experience, common sense and manufacturers' recommendations. As an example, if we take the sections of a car that we discussed, you might decide that every three months you will check the bodywork for rust, as the chance of it deteriorating within one month is minimal. However, every six months might be too long a time period. Likewise, you would check the fuel level as an ongoing item, not every three months. So to reiterate, there are two criteria for the frequency.

1. What is the amount of time required between checks that degradation can be observed in?
2. How long will the machine run for if the system is not working?

The time periods most commonly used are the following:

Shift, Daily, Weekly, Monthly, Quarterly, 6-Monthly, Annually.

Generally, all checks can be fitted into one of these periods, and they are a lot easier to work with than periods of, say, every three days or 10 times per year.

The 'Who' aspect depends on a combination of the skill level required, experience and safety aspects. You would not want an operator checking all of the electrical connections or that the roof crane is mounted correctly, would you? Similarly, there is no point in having a CNC operator check your furnaces.

Try and de-skill the jobs as far as possible, engineer the skills out if you can with automation.

The 'How' side of things can be split into two groups:

- **Internal** – actions that must be carried out with the machine switched off.
- **External** – actions that can be carried out while the machine is still running.

You obviously want to carry out as many checks as possible whilst the machine is running, as this creates less downtime as well as providing the opportunity to implement a few simple engineering improvements.

With the TPM checks, you should try and ensure that they are all external.

In addition, the chances are that you will want to carry out pre-production checks, so we will also be considering start-up checks.

You also need to decide what action to take if the check fails. Using the car analogy once again, if you were low on fuel you would carry on with the journey and re-fuel at a suitable time, but if there was a flat tyre you would not set off until you had fitted the spare tyre.

5. Brief the Workforce

You are now in possession of the completed Master Reference Table. Before this is split up into the various smaller check sheets for the specific skills groups, you must run it by the workforce. Three main reasons for this:

1. they will pick up on items that the team have missed
2. they will eliminate or combine items that the team have included
3. they will know that the checks put forward are of their own making.

In general, you should expect the Master Reference Table to shrink slightly after this.

If you are briefing the electricians in two separate groups, split by shifts possibly, then show each group the team's master reference and take notes of any suggested alterations. Discuss group 1 alterations with group 2 and vice versa to come to a common consensus.

After the alterations have been completed, have each skills group sign off their own checks. This then passes responsibility over to them – they have decided what the checks should be. They now have a direct involvement. It becomes their project.

The team is now in a position to start constructing the specific skills group check sheets. The examples above in the Master Reference Table are designed to give you a basic feel for TPM with a piece of equipment that most of us are familiar with, the car. The time periods that were initiated on the Master Reference Table were Ongoing, Daily, Weekly and Monthly. There were two people responsible for the checks, the Driver and the Mechanic. There are a number of ways that we can play this.

Firstly, we can consider putting all of the Driver checks onto one sheet and all of the Mechanic checks onto another sheet. The other extreme is we use an Ongoing, Daily, Weekly and Monthly check sheet for the Driver and the same for the Mechanic. This would result in a lot of paperwork.

We need to find a balance.

What I have done in the following sheet is detail all of the checks that the driver must perform in the week, keeping the reference number from the Master Reference Table.

The second sheet shows the weekly and monthly checks that the Mechanic must perform.

The check boxes on the right hand side have either been shaded or left blank depending on whether a check is required or not. These blank boxes should be initialled once the check has been performed. (See 'Trial', below).

Remember, the boxes for ongoing checks do not have to be completed unless something goes wrong. In the case of the Driver table, item 11 can be ignored until a window actually shatters. Then you would enter 'B' to show that it is Broken and then see a windscreen specialist. It is important that the problem is noted, as it may be a frequent problem and if it is noted an investigation into the occurrences can start. In some cases you may want the operator to sign across all 'ongoing' boxes at the end of the shift to show that there were no problems.

All sheets should also have a reference number and all alterations noted, with a new reference number allocated – e.g. XYZ-1 to XYZ-2. (See 'Monitor', below).

Driver TPM Checks

Ref. XYY-1

Machine number: L225LUG　　Machine description: Vauxhall Astra LS　　Week commencing Monday: xx/xx/200-

Ref	What to check for	How to check	Condition to meet	Action if failed	Driver to enter O, B, M, F, R Or I						
					Mon	Tue	Wed	Thu	Fri	Sat	Sun
Ongoing checks											
11	Present	Visual	All windows are fitted	See windscreen specialist							
15	Aesthetically good	Visual	Fitted correctly and no damage	Repair/replace							
16	Window winder works	Operate	Windows move up and down	Repair							
19	Mirrors in good condition	Visual	Mirrors present and undamaged	Assess damage - ignore/replace/repair							
20	Arial	Visual and operation	Present and receiving FM	Replace/repair or check connections							
Daily checks											
1	Oil level	Use dipstick	Within dipstick parameters	Fill/drain to within parameters							
2	Water level	Visual	Reaches level on water container	Fill to level immediately							
8	Clean	Visual	No build-up of dirt on glass	Clean							
9	Working	Visual	Bulbs work when switched on	Replace broken bulbs							
Weekly checks											
4	Tyre pressure	Use pressure gauge	Within 28-30 psi	Inflate/deflate to parameters							
5	Tyre tread thickness	Use tread gauge	Within legal requirements	Replace immediately							
6	Tyre wear	Visual	No flat areas in central section	Replace immediately							
7	Tyre damage	Visual	No foreign bodies or ripped	Replace immediately							
14	Clean	Visual and touch	No dust/dirt on fittings	Clean interior							

Only complete when a problem

Each check to be completed on a daily basis

Only completed when the boxes are not shaded

Notes and comments:

This sheet will be retained by the Driver all week, with a new sheet being issued on the Monday morning

Mechanic TPM Checks

Ref. XYY-1

Machine number: L225LUG   Machine description: Vauxhall Astra LS   Week commencing Monday: xx/xx/200-

Ref	What to check for	How to check	Condition to meet	Action if failed	Mechanic to enter O, B, M, F, R or I				
					1	8	15	22	29
Weekly checks									
10	Light glass not chipped	Visual	Glass is free from damage	Replace light housing					
12	Window glass not chipped	Visual	No damage to the glass	Replace/repair					
17	Bodywork free from dents	Visual	No dents in bodywork	Assess damage - ignore/replace/re					
Monthly checks									
3	Fan belt tension	Touch	Movement less than 1"	Tighten					
13	Sealed correctly	Visual	Water does not leak into car	See windscreen specialist					
18	Rust	Visual	No rust in bodywork	Repair damaged areas					
21	Towbar	Visual	Present and connected correctly	Replace or refit correctly					

These boxes contain the dates of each day in the month that the checks are carried out on, generally one week apart

Notes and comments:

This sheet will be used by the Mechanic for one month and therefore should be kept in a safe location

6. Run out TPM in a trial area

As with most projects of this nature, there is no point in trying to implement them across the entire workplace in one go. A small problem may be magnified twenty-fold. The strain placed overnight on resources may be crippling. It is important to select a trial area, say three or four machines, to ensure that the system functions correctly.

Ensure that the people involved are aware of the entire situation. Everyone must be a part of the team. Pick a specific start date, usually a Monday, and have the project team on hand when the first set of checks are carried out. This will give added confidence to the operator, show that the team are serious and, most important, will allow the team to answer any questions and observe any problems.

What do the Skills Groups actually do?

Whoever is carrying out the checks will have in their possession a copy of the relevant sheet. They simply have to match up the blank boxes with the day the check is required on. In the Driver sheet above, the driver has to carry out checks 1, 2, 8 and 9 every day and check 4 every Monday. Simple.

It is suggested that the checks are carried out towards the end of the time period. This is because if all checks are done in the morning and a few problems appear in the afternoon then some confusion may occur on the sheets. If a problem does happen, then it should be noted immediately in case the checker forgets by the end of the shift.

What are O, B, M, F, R and I?

Usually there are five main outcomes of checks. However, if a generic check sheet is being used a sixth will be introduced. The possible outcomes are:

1. A check has been carried out and the desired condition *has been met.*
   E.g. the windscreen has not been shattered.
2. A check has been carried out but the condition *has not been met.* The item will need attention.
   E.g. the windscreen has been shattered.
3. A check has been carried out, the condition *has not been met*, however the machine is *still capable of running*. It will need repairing at a later date.
   E.g. a small oil leak is evident from the stain on the road.
4. A check has been carried out, the condition *has not been met*, however

the problem was *corrected by the operator*. It has to be highlighted though, for if the problem is fairly frequent there is clearly a need for maintenance to investigate.

E.g. there was a flat tyre. It was changed without the need for a trained mechanic.

5. A start-up check was scheduled, however shifts are currently running at 24 hours so there are *no opportunities to carry out the check*. If the machine is running then there is no need to check items such as electricity, gas and water supplies, which tend to make up the bulk of the start-up checks. You do not want to stop production if it is obviously running well. Start-up checks may be called 'pre-production checks' in some companies, however in the main pre-production tends to refer to items such as paperwork, correct product codes being used, all quality gauges on station and the like, with a greater emphasis on the production management rather than the engineering side of things.

   E.g. you are driving along when you realise that you should have checked the tyres for damage.
6. The sixth check is used on generic sheets, where a series of machines may all be basically the same however there are slight variations. Even though some checks *may not be relevant* to a certain machine, it makes sense to have one sheet that all the operators are familiar with. This should be indicated on the check sheet to show that it is not relevant rather than just not carried out.

   E.g. the sheet says to check the condition of your tow bar, however you do not have one fitted.

Each of these possibilities requires a specific mark for identification, and each of the marks should be clearly distinguishable from the others. For instance you would not consider using a capital 'O' to represent OK, or criteria 1, above, and a zero '0' to represent that the check was not carried out, criteria 5 above. They are too similar. So, what should be used? Try the following, for the criteria mentioned:

1. '**O**' to represent the condition has been met. It is **OK**.
2. '**B**' represents that the condition has not been met. It is **Broken**.
3. '**M**' shows that **Maintenance** is required however the machine is running.
4. '**F**' represents that the issue has been **Fixed**, generally by the operator.

5. '**R**' indicates that the machine was **Running**, so the check was not possible or unnecessary.
6. '**I**' represents that the check is **Irrelevant**.

Each of these letters is clearly distinct from the others, whether in capital or lower case, and will therefore not cause miss-understanding when the check sheets are evaluated.

The sheets should be kept in a very visual but at the same time safe location. Anyone should be in a position to check that the TPM checks have been completed at the specified times.

7. Implement across the factory (if relevant)

Once you are happy that all is well within the trial area, and within a certain time period, it is time for the next big step – the implementation across the factory. Once again I would suggest that you go slow on this, increasing only a few machines at a time rather than taking one huge leap. Monitor the success as each area is introduced, keeping a regular series of project team meetings to discuss any concerns. The project has not been completed yet, it is just being increased, so the team should still be intact.

As before, ensure that everyone involved is confident in what is expected of them.

Once you are confident that the implementation has been successful, the following should be considered. There may arise in some cases the need to bring in outside specialists to perform annual services or overhauls. Rather than relying on them to contact you, which they generally are keen to do given the amount of 'phone calls and site visits that sales people carry out, it is important that they are aware of these requirements and reminded of them.

A simple wall calendar will suffice, with important dates marked off and annotated. For our example of the car this will cover MOT, road tax and insurance. You may say that this is an obvious statement to make, but I'm sure that we all know someone who has forgotten to renew their insurance or MOT certificate. For something as vital and legally important as these to be forgotten is a poor state of affairs, however when you may have 40 machines to consider, plus additional secondary plant, it is easy to forget.

8. Monitor

The maintenance department should already be collecting the information on the sheets or the sheets themselves depending on the time period that they are used for. This will highlight areas of concern that may have to be addressed within a short time span, such as recurring problems that the operator has corrected. (Marked with 'F'). The sheets should be checked for recurring problems on a regular basis, this being site specific and dependant on the set-up that you have, and the information fed back into the TPM system. You may find that you have to increase or decrease check frequencies. This is important. Place a responsible individual in charge of this, with regular feedback sessions to the original project team.

Any alterations to the Master Reference Table should be noted. No sheets should be altered unless the Master has been altered. This will reduce confusion that may arise and ensure that all alterations have been passed by the project team.

What to do when something goes wrong

If an operator sees a problem and can not resolve it themselves, then obviously the maintenance department is required. Something is broken or in need of maintenance. In most cases this is simply a matter of finding and informing the mechanic. If you work in a large manufacturing plant however, this may cause problems and a simple way around this is a general information board.

The operator marks on the board the machine number, the type of concern (Broken or Maintenance required) and the nature of the fault. The time that the fault was reported should also be noted. This allows us to determine the reaction time of the maintenance department and calculate whether more resources are required. For instance, if the operator reports a problem at 17:00, maintenance attend at 17:30 due to other problems within the plant, and complete repairs at 17:35, then you may decide that you need to increase maintenance cover. (Until the TPM kicks in properly.)

There should also be a space on the board for priority machines in the event of more than one machine requiring attention. This board will be in a location that is convenient for the operators and in an area the maintenance department frequent, such as the workshops or canteen.

This information will also be noted within the 'Notes and comments' section of the check sheets. From here it will be picked up in the regular checks and used as feedback to the TPM checks and frequencies.

It may look like the following.

Maintenance Required

Date: Xx/xx/200-

Priority machines 1. XA 2. XB 3. YA 4. ZC

No	B or M	Description	Reported	Attended	Completed	Signed	Comments
XC	M	Oil leak	08.30	08.35	08.40	PH	Blah
GA	M	Water temperature high	09.23	10.05	10.10	CB	Blah
BA	B	Safety cover loose	10.20	10.20	10.45	PH	Blah
YA	M	Slider jammed	14.15	15.21	15.35	CB	Blah
XA	B	Drive belt snapped	14.18	14.29	15.20	CB/PH	Blah

This lets the other engineers know that someone is in attendance

B or M allows priorities to be determined

SMED – Single Minute Exchange of Dies

As with all aspects of a companies operations, you must ask:

'What are our customers willing to pay for?'

The items that they are not willing to pay for have to be borne by the company. If they are willing to pay for excessive downtime, fair enough. If they are not willing to pay, they will go to a supplier who is tackling the problem, your competitors will reduce costs, improve customer service and you will lose out. You can carry on the way you are ... or you can keep any improvement savings for yourself.

SMED – What do we mean by this?

Simply, we are trying to reduce the amount of stoppage time taken up by changeovers to a single minute. Having said that, it would be more correct to say single minutes – less than ten.

Having seen the diagrams in the TPM section, you will know that in most cases, a machines working hours can be split into three distinct sections:

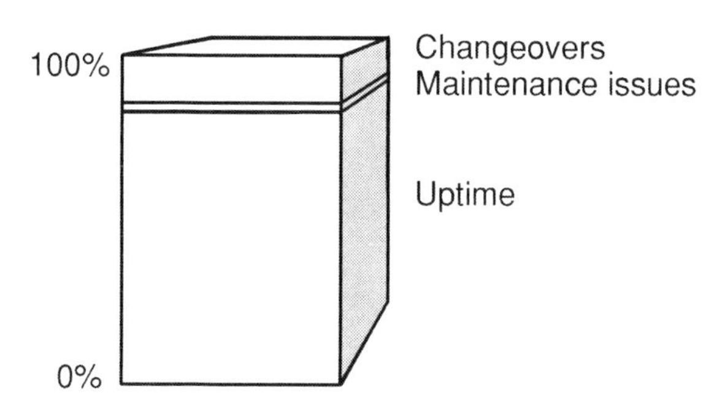

This is the second diagram from the TPM section, showing a reduction in maintenance related downtime. (As mentioned, in heavier industries there may also be a lot of time lost through issues concerning dies, such as specific maintenance problems. However, in the main, there are only really three areas. Die issues should be addressed through a specialised maintenance program – TPM.)

What we aim to do through SMED is decrease the amount of time lost through changeovers and add that same amount of time to production hours, as shown in the next diagram, below:

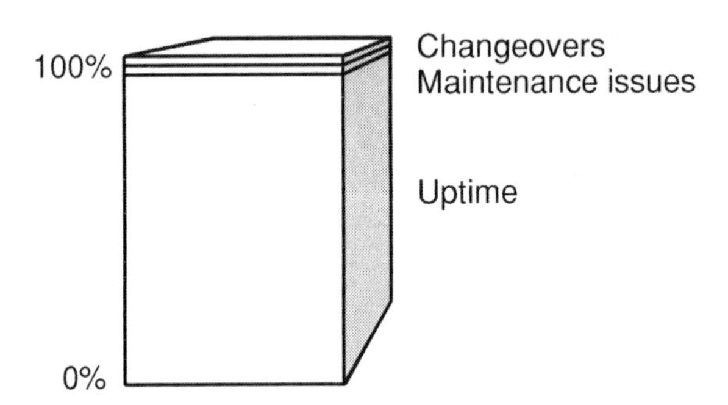

As you will see, the uptime shown here is greatly increased from that shown in the first diagram in the TPM section.

We must not think purely of Downtime as the amount of time the machine is switched off for. We measure changeover times as last good component to first good component. It is essential that you remember that – '*first good component*'. In some cases, a huge amount of changeover time is taken up with tweaking the set-up once you think that you have finished.

By following the SMED principles, we can drastically reduce our downtime, leading not only to greater productivity but providing benefits in the following fields:

- increased flexibility
- less need for inventory
- decreased chance of large scale defects
- greater service levels.

Increased Flexibility

If a changeover takes a long time, then the traditional thought is to run the machine with the one product for a long period of time. Indeed, in some cases, companies may have a large capital machine running only the one product. They can not afford the amount of downtime required to change over and still meet their customer requirements. The changeover would make their

Cycle Time greater than the Takt Time, once CPE had been calculated.

However if there is a problem with raw material supplies, die condition, secondary equipment, quality gauges and the like, it is not always possible to run that machine. Unless of course you can change to another set of dies.

Less need for inventory

Once again, if you think that it is only economical to changeover every week as opposed to every day, or hour, and you run five products off of the one machine, then naturally when changeover time comes around you require four weeks stock, plus safety stock requirements, to continue to supply your customer. If you change over every day, you only require four days' worth of stock for each component. Big difference, isn't it?

Decreased chance of large scale defects

This will obviously happen naturally if there is less need for inventory. Following the last example you will have four days' worth of bad stock instead of four weeks' worth.

Greater service levels

This occurs due to the fact that your customers are forever changing their minds as to what they actually want. (Sound familiar?) If you can change your planning requirements at a moment's notice, then your customers remain happy and profitable. You are not only helping them with their problems, but also creating shorter lead times and making them look more efficient in the eyes of their customers.

Let's look at a simple example.

A machine provides a production base for 8 separate components, and the average changeover time is two hours, with one changeover happening per day.

Over an eight hour shift (440 minutes allowing for a total of forty minutes for breaks) your takt time is 60 seconds, for all components. Luckily, the cycle time is 6 seconds, taking into consideration CPE. This also applies to all components. You will already know that you have to manufacture eight days' worth of components at one time in order to keep supplying your customers. (The actual day's production plus seven days' stock before the component runs once more). You also know that you have to provide overtime for changeovers to happen.

- ☐ 8 hour shift minus 40 minutes break times = 26,400 seconds production time
- ☐ 26,400 seconds minus 7,200 for the changeover = 19,200 seconds actual production time
- ☐ TT = 60, therefore each shift requires 440 components. (26,400/60=440)

One changeover every 8 days requires 3,520 components produced at a time. However, the actual production time of 19,200 seconds equals a shift rate of only 3,200 components, therefore the shortfall of 320 components requires 1,920 seconds of overtime per shift. (32 minutes).

If the changeover times were radically reduced, what would happen? Let's take 90% off of the total time. Don't be shocked, 90% is a very achievable figure for the first time you consider any set-up. If you cannot find 90% waste, get another job.

- ☐ 8 hour shift minus 40 minutes break times = 26,400 seconds production time
- ☐ 26,400 seconds minus 720 for the changeover = 25,680 seconds actual production time
- ☐ TT = 60, therefore each shift requires 440 components

Eight changeovers per day requires 440 components produced at a time, or a total run time of 2,640 seconds.

An additional 720 seconds for the changeover gives us 3,360 seconds. Eight separate runs per shift requires 26,880 seconds, or 448 minutes. OK, so this is still eight minutes overtime, but your inventory is 10% of what it was plus all of the additional bonuses mentioned. And what is eight minutes per shift at the end of the week?

40 minutes per week, against 32 minutes per shift beforehand. And I would hope that the next time you carried out a SMED exercise in this area, you will find at least a further minute to take off the time.

This is a very simple example, but in the real world, you may need to carry out a great deal of number crunching in order to see the overall benefits and calculate your goals as far as ongoing exercises are concerned.

How is SMED implemented?

Lets get down to the nitty gritty. The two main types of time in a changeover reduction exercise are:

Internal – actions that must be carried out with the machine switched off.
External – actions that can be carried out while the machine is still running.

In the main, before an initial analysis of the situation, all of the work is carried out during the changeover – there is no pre-planning. After the analysis it will be seen that Internal is generally sandwiched between two lots of External:

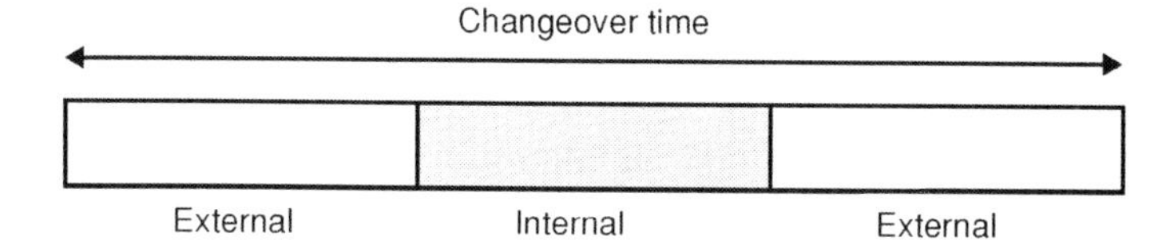

What you have to do is change as much Internal time as possible to External, and then concentrate on reducing the size of both.

The main steps are as follows:

1. Observe and time the existing changeover procedures.
2. Clearly define Internal and External actions.
3. Convert Internal to External and implement actions to decrease both types of time.
4. Observe and time the new changeover procedures.

   Go to Number 1 and start again. When you are happy that no more can be done, go to Number 1 and start again. When you are happy that no more can be done, go to Number 1 and start again. When you are happy that no more can be done, carry on.
5. Implement Standard Work Lists.

   Two months later, go to Number 1.

If these simple steps are followed and maintained, the % reductions on successive changeovers should resemble the following graph:

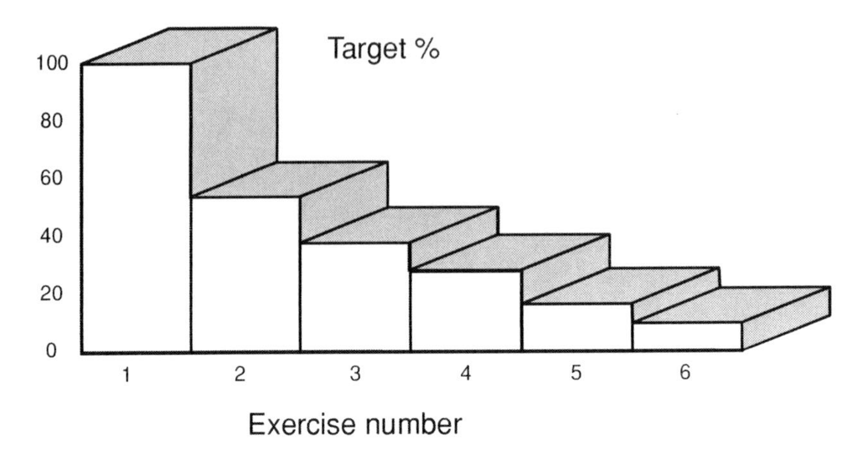

This is what the team should be aiming to achieve by the end of the week, whether in actual practise or through simulation of longer term changes. The main Japanese consultants, the very best in the world, believe that 59/60th's of a changeover time can be eliminated, so the graph above is achievable.

In Slightly more Detail

The team should be made up of a number of disciplines, for instance at least one operator (obviously), a mechanical fitter, a toolmaker and a line supervisor. In the vast majority of cases the operator will be the person who carries out the changeover, but in the event that they do not then the changeover specialist should not replace the operator in the team, both should be present. (If a skilled person is required to carry out your changes, remember that longer term the quicker the changeovers become the easier they should be, so it should be possible to de-skill the job to such an extent that shop-floor, unskilled operators can carry them out.)

For the purpose of making the writing slightly easier, I will refer to the Operator as doing the changeover.

Once the exercise location and the team has been selected, they should spend a bit of time in the actual area getting a feel for the location and machinery involved. The operator will talk through with the team what a typical changeover comprises, once again so everyone is slightly more familiar with the process.

Only then will the operator start. The other team members will be responsible for the following:

a. Filling in the Single Task Observation Sheet with times and observations.
b. Using a Location Chart to track the route the operator follows.
c. Filling in the Time Observation Sheet.
d. Making personal observations and queries.

The Single Task Observation Sheet, Location Chart and Time Observation Sheet are shown a few pages on, with information entered and annotation provided. Before we go on any further though, the **Single Task Observation Sheet** is completed in the following manner.

1. As soon as the operator starts their changeover the timer starts the stop-watch. It is important that all actions relating to a changeover are recorded. It is vitally important to note that the stop watch is not switched off until the first good component is produced. *The stop watch is used to obtain a running time and not individual action times.*
2. On the Single Task Observation Sheet the Timer will note the action being performed by the operator. (Do this as the changeover occurs, do not write the actions down beforehand as the operator inevitably will not follow the route they think they will follow). Once this action is complete the time is noted in the Run Time column. The stop watch is not switched off but kept running.
3. The Timer carries on in this manner, describing all the actions and the *time when each action is completed.* The Timer may also note any personal observations or queries.

We have already said that the changeover is from the last good to the first good. If the operator goes for a coffee or to the toilet then include this in the timings.

All actions must be noted

While the Timer is carrying out their task, the other team members will be carrying out theirs.

The purpose of the **Location Chart** is to monitor the route the operator follows. A brief outline of the working area is drawn on the chart and the observer simply draws the route followed by the setter.

This is used to clearly provide a record of the amount of walking and movement involved in a changeover, and allows the team to determine the optimum position for tooling, tools, gauges and the like.

There are descriptions here of the actions regarding movement away from the main centre of activity, and these should be referenced on the drawing itself, as can be seen.

Notes are beneficial and should be written in on the chart.

The **Time Observation Sheet** is used to plot the individual times of each changeover and is at this stage primarily to give straightforward information as to the progress of the team. One sheet is all that is required and is filled in after each changeover.

In the fullness of time though, the Time Observation Sheet will be used to monitor every changeover and act as a feedback to review meetings (weekly or monthly management reviews?) on the sustained progress of the event. Hence the column titled 'Description and Comments' that is used to highlight any concerns that may have occurred during a changeover. If these are properly documented it gives us the opportunity to address them as part of the review meetings.

The other team members are generally observing and making personal notes.

Step by Step through the Single Task Observation Sheet

1. Once the changeover has been completed the next stage is to calculate the length of time that each action required. This is done by simply subtracting time 1 from time 2 to obtain the action time for 2, time 2 from time 3 to obtain the action time for 3 and so on. These times are then written in the 'Elem. Time' column.
2. Once this has been completed the team must decide what are Internal and what are External actions. Remember:

   Internal – actions that must be carried out with the machine switched off.
   External – actions that can be carried out while the machine is still running.

   Actions such as collecting tooling or completing paperwork should all be External. Mark these down on the sheet in the 'Int. or Ext.' column. Don't bother too much with actions such as waiting for the machine to actually stop running or to start up once more.

3. From here the team can plot the Individual Element Time that each action took. This is once again a visual guide to the elements in the changeover, showing at a glance where resources should be focused. (Hint – target the longest, internal rows first.) Highlighter pens are good for this, with the Internal being red and the External being green.

Each of the blocks in this table represents a period of time. The team must decide what this period will be before plotting, these periods being calculated to provide the most visually beneficial table. For instance, if all of your action times are below 5 minutes except for one which is at 20 minutes, I would go with periods that cover 5 minutes. Physically write in the row that the one that goes off of the scale is 20 minutes in length.

Once the changeover is complete, the Single Task Observation Sheet, Location Chart and Time Observation Sheet should look like those on the following pages. These were written out for an automatically running metal heading machine where the operator was intended to react to problems and ensure that the base material, in this case 12mm thick metal wire, did not run out. They have been simplified for our general overview.

Sheet type - Kaizen, Single Task, Repetitive Task, Combination Sheet, Location, Problem Listing and Pareto, Time Observation

Location: Heading m/c No 5 | Observer: WSR | Process: Carding

Date: 3/11/200-

Observation: Full changeover

Component: 3/8" to 1/4" Toggle

Time: 15.30

Numbered	Description	Run time	Elem time	Int Ext	Individual element plot 10 20 30 40 50 60 70 80 90 100 110
1	Machine stopped and comes to a halt	0:10	0:10		
2	Paperwork	1:30	1:20	E	
3	Remove existing and collect new quality gauges	2:10	0:40	E	
4	Remove guards	3:40	1:30	I	
5	Collect tools	4:20	0:40	E	
6	Slacken dies	5:50	1:30	I	
7	Remove fixture s	6:20	0:30	I	
8	Replace new fixtures	7:00	0:40	I	
9	Tighten dies	7:30	0:30	I	
10	Replace guards	9:00	1:30	I	
11	Paperwork	10:20	1:20	E	
12	Start machine	10:30	0:10		

Sheet type - Kaizen, Single Task, Repetitive Task, Combination Sheet, Location, Problem Listing and Pareto, Time Observation

Location: Heading m/c No 5 | Observer: WSR | Process: Carding

Date: 3/11/200- | Observation: Full changeover | Component: 3/8" to 1/4" Toggle

Time: 15.30

Numbered	Description				Each square represents 1 metre
1	Paperwork				
2	Remove existing and collect new quality gauges				
3	Collect tools				
4	Replace new fixtures				
5	Paperwork				

Sheet type - Kaisen, Single Task, Repetitive Task, Combination Sheet, Location, Problem Listing and Paretto, Time Observation

Location: Heading m/c No 5 Observer: WSR Process: Carding

Date: 3/11/200- Observation: Full changeover Component: 3/8" to 1/4" Toggle

Time: 15.30

Date & time	Description and comments	C/O time	Obs		Changeover time in minutes 1	2	3	4	5	6	7	8	9	10	11	12
3/11 15.30	Full changeover - 3/8" to 1/4" toggle - no problems	10:30	CTB													

Beginning the improvements

We have started to gather information on the changeover as it is at present. The next stage is to start reducing that time. There is no clear step-by-step process through this, as each exercise is unique to a certain extent, so the main focus of this will be teamwork and brainstorming. I can not tell you how to come up with good ideas – that is down to the skills and experience of the team that has been chosen.

Internal Time

The first action to carry out is to convert as much Internal time as possible to External. In the example above items 2, 3, 5 and 11 are all external activities. Make sure that these are clearly identified as such and incorporated into the next changeover as Externals. There is so much to be gained from this simple step, and it is all down to **planning**.

If the team follows these simple rules, quick hits can be obtained, increasing the spirit of the team and leading to early results.

Where are we now?

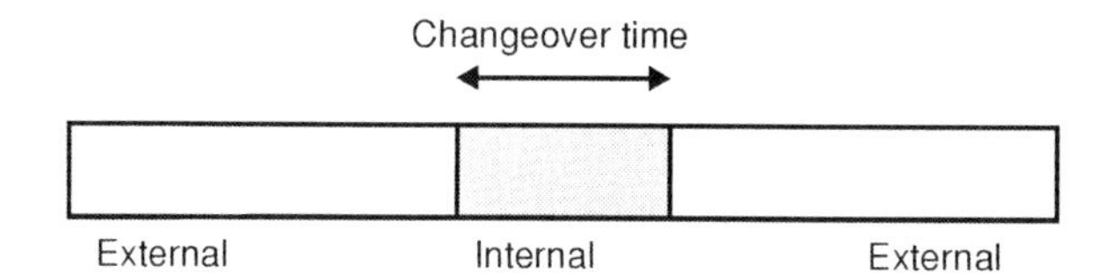

The team must now set about trying to reduce the time taken for the remaining Internal activities, actions that can only be done whilst the machine is switched off. One thing to look at here, from our example, would be the time taken to remove and replace the guarding.

Can we fit quick release clamps to it? These would have to be interlocked obviously, but would reduce the times from 3 minutes to a matter of seconds. Let us say 20 seconds, purely due to the fact that that was the actual time it took once quick release clamps had been fitted.

One big area to look at is the slackening and tightening of the dies. Why is there such a huge difference in time here? Surely they should be the same, as all you are doing is reversing the actions?

The team must look at a host of options, such as:

- quick release mechanisms on the fixtures

- quick release couplings on hydraulics and pneumatics (self-seal units are a must)
- basket changes for the dies
- numeric positioning devices.

And the big one …

- tooling redesign if applicable.

'Over-engineering' not only applies to products, it applies to all aspects of the company, and tooling should be no different.

Look also at non-value-adding actions within internal time. For instance, you may need an allen key to slacken the cap screws that hold the die in place. To a certain extent, slackening them is adding value to the actual SMED process.

What isn't adding value is deciding you need an allen key, opening your toolbox, rummaging about, selecting the correct key from the plastic holder and finally fitting into the cap screw. Within each internal time action that you have identified, there will be an opportunity to break it down to smaller components. A lot of time can be saved from doing this.

Where should that leave us?

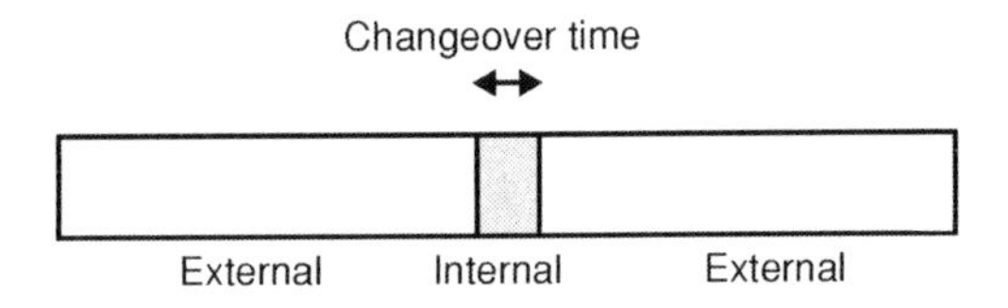

As can be seen the external times have grown slightly due to internal times being converted to external, however the internal times have reduced significantly.

External Time

From looking at the last little diagram, you may say what is the point in removing external time if the machine is back up and running? When these external elements are carried out whilst the machine is running, the operator is not watching the machine. Time is not necessarily lost, but the operator is not carrying out his job.

Removal of external time can be done in two main ways:

1. Organise the changeover so all external activities are performed by other personnel. For instance, tooling and quality gauges could be delivered by the relevant departments, not collected.
2. Place equipment where it is needed. It will have been noticed that the Location Sheet has highlighted areas where the operator was walking great distances, for instance to collect tools (40 seconds).The operator was required to move away from the machine. Why were they not on a board in front of him, within reaching distance?

From the Observation Sheet, it can be seen that External time takes up 4 minutes out of a total of 10 minutes and thirty seconds.

The removal and replacing of the guards takes a further three minutes, compared with an actual time spent working on the dies and fixtures of 3 minutes and 10 seconds.

In this example nearly 40% of the time is wasted.

Why do the Quality Department not bring new gauges to the machine before the changeover commences? This should be easy enough to organise. The Quality Department obviously know that a changeover is about to occur, otherwise they wouldn't have the gauges ready, so why do they not deliver? Why is the paperwork in that position? Once again, there is waste. One thing that wasn't shown was that the tools were not replaced. (Remember what I said about writing the actions down as they occur, not as the operator thinks they will occur?) This will add another 40 seconds to the operator's time when the machine is actually running. It is important to consider these extra actions.

And this is a good changeover. As I mentioned, a large part of any changeover is taken up with adjusting once the machine is up and running again, hence the principle of 'last good, first good'. I have not shown any adjusting and we have already highlighted 40% waste through removal of External time.

Where does that leave us now?

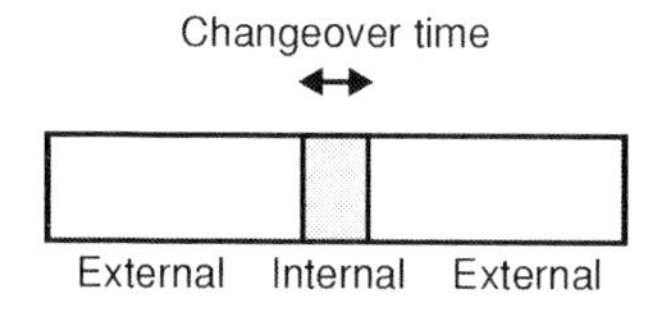

Here are a few items to consider when looking at Internal and External:

Less adjustment, less errors

- ☑ No trial components. The first one off should be the first good one off.
- ☑ Once everything is in place, that should be it. Don't 'tweak' anything. If this has to be done, fit a scale to allow fast and accurate positioning, think about dead stops or dowels for positioning. Analyse the defects in the first few off and tackle the problem through CEDAC if required.

Prepare in advance

- ☑ Have jigs, tooling, tools etc near the machine.
- ☑ Ensure everything is identified, e.g. die numbers etc.

Make sure everything works

- ☑ Make sure you have the correct equipment.
- ☑ Use time and labour saving devices – air guns, quick release devices, however…
- ☑ …the fewer tools required, the better.
- ☑ Is it possible for two people to work together? If so, remember safety.
- ☑ Try to make all paperwork as generic as possible.

Bolts are our enemies

- ☑ Can you fit numeric counters for accurate, first time positioning?

Once again

- ☑ Review what the team has discovered. Let everyone have their say, it is after all a team effort and no one person should try and bully their ideas through. (If they are as intelligent as they seem to think they are, why aren't they in charge of the first manned Mars mission?) No idea is too small, big or stupid. Even if something sounds stupid, it may trigger an idea in someone else.
- ☑ Make good use of the Kaizen Monthly, take a detailed note of what is decided and implemented, whether good or bad.
- ☑ If the team is satisfied that there are enough options to be tried out, a Single Task Observation Sheet should be written up detailing the exact series of actions, in the order that the team has decreed.

Once these options have been put into place, retime the changeover. (Note – the changeovers should be like for like. That is to say there is no point in timing a changeover that involves half of the maintenance department and comparing it with a changeover that involves one person.)

Do not worry about internal actions possibly being the same as they were previously, some of the details here may take time, items have lead times or you may have to fabricate something especially. Try to simulate items and actions as far as possible to see if they will actually work, for instance have people holding the guards in place instead of them being bolted in place.

If you do try this, **ensure that the machine is completely isolated beforehand**. You know how long it takes to switch off, so there is no need to actually run the machine with the guards not safely fastened.

- ☑ Decide on a realistic saving in time – 20 seconds for clamps as opposed to 3 minutes for the existing method.
- ☑ Complete the sheets as before and monitor the impact of the changes tried out.
- ☑ Once again, review your findings and react to them. Trim a few seconds here and a few seconds there. It will get more difficult as you go along, as the 80-20 rule will apply:

80% of the savings take 20% of the time, and vice versa.

- ☑ Retime the changeover and implement ideas.
- ☑ Take note in the Kaizen Monthly.
- ☑ Retime the changeover and implement ideas.
- ☑ Take note in the Kaizen Monthly.

That was not a printing error. Keep doing it until the team are happy that no more can be gained. (You will find extra in 2 months time when you go back to review the situation.)

What happens next should be obvious. If the operator follows a set order of actions in the final changeover that the team are happy with, then they must follow that order in all subsequent changeovers.

Finally a **Standard Work** list must be written out that clearly shows each step an operator must follow to maintain this level of efficiency.

If possible write it in stone. This should be adhered to at all times during a changeover. Even though it is written in stone it doesn't mean that the exercise is finished. If someone comes up with a better way of doing things, then do it. Do it properly, with the original SMED team if possible, but do it.

This is the only time that a Standard Work list should be altered.

Here are a few hints for the event

- ☑ Make sure everyone knows the principles of SMED.
- ☑ Everyone should be familiar with the area of the event.
- ☑ All paperwork must be available.
- ☑ Pens, stopwatches, calculators, clipboards – do you have them?
- ☑ Are people familiar with the way the stopwatch works? (Not as stupid as it sounds).
- ☑ Act as a team, no bullying, but you can coach.
- ☑ Do not go into the event thinking that you know the solution. Act on what you see.
- ☑ Do not be afraid of failing, as long as you can gain experience and information.
- ☑ Make good use of string, sellotape, plasticine etc if a quick trial is needed.
- ☑ If available, videotape the event. It's amazing what you will pick up that the eye missed.
- ☑ At the end of the exercise, the team should be in possession of the following:
  - a series of *Single Task Observation Sheets*
  - a corresponding number of *Location Sheets*
  - a *Time Observation Sheet*
  - a *Standard Work List*
  - a *Kaizen Monthly Newspaper* detailing everything the team implemented and any outstanding items.

  If possible:
  - a before and after *video* of the changeover

  If required:
  - Changeover Preparation Sheet
  - Information Sheets

  (See later)

All of these should be clearly documented and kept in the kaizen office or folder for future reference.

Let us have a look at the example we were running with through this exercise. A number of areas were highlighted, such as the amount of time it took to remove and replace the guards – I said that this could be taken down to a matter of seconds, and it has been.

Another area that was picked up on was the difference in time taken between slackening the dies and tightening them – 90 seconds and 30 seconds respectively. This should have had you asking a few questions. As it turns out, there was a small mechanical problem in this area that was resolved, and when added to the fact that some power tools were introduced for this purpose, the time taken came down to 20 seconds for each.

The use of quick release clamps and couplings helped in the removal and replacement of the fixtures themselves, halving the time taken to replace them and taking a further 10 seconds off of the removal, giving a 30 second saving.

How does our final set of paperwork look now?

Sheet type - Kaizen, Single Task, Repetitive Task, Combination Sheet, Location, Problem Listing and Pareto, Time Observation

Location: Heading m/c No 5 | Observer: WSR | Process: Carding
Date: 7/11/200- | Observation: Full changeover | Component: 3/8" to 1/4" Toggle
Time: 09.15

Numbered	Description	Run time	Elem time	Int Ext	Individual element plot 10 20 30 40 50 60 70 80 90 100 110
1	Machine stopped and comes to a halt	0:10	0:10		
2	Remove guards	0:20	0:10	I	
3	Slacken dies	0:40	0:20	I	
4	Remove fixture s	1:00	0:20	I	
5	Replace new fixtures	1:20	0:20	I	
6	Tighten dies	1:40	0:20	I	
7	Replace guards	1:50	0:10	I	
8	Start machine	2:00	0:10		

Sheet type - Kaizen, Single Task, Repetitive Task, Combination Sheet, Location, Problem Listing and Pareto, Time Observation

Location: Heading m/c No 5 Observer: WSR Process: Carding

Date: 3/11/200- Observation: Full changeover Component: 3/8" to 1/4" Toggle

Time: 15.30

Numbered	Description				Each square represents 1 metre^2
1	Remove existing fixtures				
2	Replace new fixtures				

Fixtures 1 & 2

Sheet type - Kaizen, Single Task, Repetitive Task, Combination Sheet, Location, Problem Listing and Pareto, Time Observation

Location: Heading m/c No 5 | Observer: WSR | Process: Carding

Date: As shown | Observation: As shown | Component: As detailed

Time: As shown

Date & time	Description and comments	C/O time	Obs		Changeover time in minutes 1 2 3 4 5 6 7 8 9 10 11 12
3/11 15.30	Full changeover - 3/8" to 1/4" toggle - no problems	10:30	WSR		
4/11 12.45	Full changeover - 3/8" to 1/4" toggle - no problems	5:40	WSR		
5/11 09.37	Full changeover - 3/8" to 1/4" toggle - dropped spanners	4:00	CJB		
6/11 10.54	Part changeover - change head profile. Quick release jammed	2:30	WSR		
7/11 09.15	Full changeover - 3/8" to 1/4" toggle - no problems	2:00	TER		

In addition to these sheets, and to be included in the final package, there may be the need for two further items.

A Changeover Preparation Sheet must be considered, detailing all of the preparation work that has to be carried out prior to the commencement of the first set of external time. These are particularly relevant to large changeovers, where there are a lot of interconnecting systems and co-ordination is required between numerous departments – toolroom, production, quality, stores. That does not mean that they are irrelevant to small scale changeovers.

These should be signed off by someone of a senior position and must be completed within a certain time period before the changeover is planned to allow any problems to be tackled.

One sheet should be completed per changeover, and this should be kept for future reference.

If possible, try to create these sheets to be generic over a range of similar machines. This will reduce both the amount of paperwork required and any confusion that may arise as to what sheets are for what machines.

Information Sheets compliment the Changeover Preparation Sheet. They detail all of the information relevant to the dies or machine, such as clamp sizes, lifting gear required, services, location of plates, setting dimensions etc.

The example shown will accommodate the two machines that die number 8859 will run on, numbers 23 and 36.

These sheets should be kept in the area where die preparation is carried out. They should be laminated, and on display all the time for anyone to see.

These three sheets are specific to the requirements of the plant.

The following examples show a Standard Work List, Changeover Preparation Sheet and an Information Sheet:

Standard Work List

Process: Full changeover - Heading machine, Number 5
Written by: WSR Dated: 7/11/200-

	DESCRIPTION	COMMENTS
	Before the changeover	
1	Update and complete all relevant paperwork	
2	Ensure that quality gauges are in place	To be delivered by the Quality Department. See Prep sheet
3	Ensure that all tooling that is required is in place	To be delivered by the Toolroom See Prep sheet.
4	Ensure that all tools are in place	Check against shadow board
	During the changeover	
5	Switch machine off	
6	Remove the guarding	Ensure that interlocks are not damaged
7	Slacken the dies off	
8	Remove old tooling	Check beds are clean and free from damage
9	Replace with new tooling	
10	Tighten the die	
11	Replace the guarding	
	After the changeover	
12	Ensure that component is within specifications	
13	Complete paperwork	This to include amount of time required for changeover

Comments:

Items 2 and 3 to be supported by the Changeover Preparation Sheet
Average changeover time at the end of the last SMED exercise was 2 minutes
Please report any problems to supervisors
Foe additional information, please refer to last SMED documents

Changeover Preparation Sheet

The following, where required, must be in place before a changeover can start. Tick the box to confirm that they are, or enter 'NA' if Not Applicable. If any box is not marked, then explain why in the 'Comments and Problems' section. All sheets must be signed off by the Unit Manager 2 hours prior to commencing the changeover.

Machine Number :
Operator :
Date :
Number of Die coming out :
Number of Die going in :

New Die

The die must be sitting upright in a stand	
All electrical switches must be fitted	
All wiring must be in a good condition	
All cylinders must be fitted	
All quick release fittings must be in good condition	
The required eyebolts/trunions must be fitted	
All services must be connected	
All relevant quality gauges available and in the correct location	

Old Die

The required eyebolts/trunions must be fitted	
There should be a stand available for the die to be placed upright	
Safety clamps must be fitted to the die	

Lifting Gear

All chains required must be in good condition and in the area	
The crane must be available and in the area	

General

All tools required must be available.
All personnel required must be informed and available when required.
The machine area must be clean enough to accommodate the new die.

Signed off: (Business Unit Manager)

Comments and Problems:

Die Information Sheet

Die Number : 8859
Product : ZC105 sump bolts
Cylinders required : 70, 70, 65, 70

Machine Number	**23**	**36**
Bush Type	1400T	1400T
Bush bore	112mm	112mm
Packing Ring	60mm	60mm
Register Offset	300mm	300mm
Stem	ST-2	ST-2
Stem Packing Plates	Any	Any
Tip	112mm	112mm
Ejector Bar Number	8859-1	8859-1
Maximum Ejection	N/A	N/A
Shot Height	300mm	300mm
Robot Program	GP1-2	GP1-2

Strap sizes :145mm
Trunions :4 off 2" UNC
Stand Number :ST-8859
Electrical Switches :10 off CF-3

One of The Rover Group's suppliers had some Rover kaizen engineers on site. It took the supplier 8 hours to change a production line from one component to the next. Once the engineers had finished, it took 29 seconds.

Even better – Nissan Motors UK Ltd. are very good at kaizen, and their production facility in Tyne-and-Wear is one of the leanest, if not the leanest, in Europe. As an example of the large statement below, one of their production lines can handle two separate models of car. Simultaneously. No changeover required.

So, remember -

The best changeover is the one that doesn't have to be done at all.

Poka Yoke – Mistake Proofing

This section varies from the others in that there is no paperwork or simple exercises to follow. All that we are going to do is describe the principles and the benefits of poka-yoke. The rest is up to you.

The method is designed to initially compliment quality inspection and control within the workplace, as it is impractical to alter a complete quality system overnight. However, the ultimate goal of poka-yoke is to replace the need for quality inspection – the defects should highlight themselves.

Systems are generally designed so that if the first operation is faulty then it will be impossible to start the next operation. This is achieved through a combination of careful planning of the order in which operations are completed and good engineering innovation. For this reason, it tends to be used in machining operations and assembly rather than areas where there is a need for fine finishes or aesthetics.

One of Ohno's colleagues at Toyota, Shigeo Shingo, classified quality systems into three main categories.

Judgement inspection – You judge whether the product is good enough to pass on to the customer. Big problem with this? There are a number of them. If you take a sample, then there is the chance that poor quality product gets through. If you inspect 100%, it is time consuming and expensive. And the biggest problem with Judgement inspection? You have already made the product, invested time and money into it, only to scrap or re-work it. Not a good situation.

Informative inspection – Statistical Production Control would come under this heading. Basically, you monitor the components and react to trends that start to develop. This is still not quick enough though, and once again there is the possibility that you will let poor quality product through.

Source inspection – The component is inspected at source, and if you are going to do this you might as well do it in line, with the operator carrying out 100% inspection otherwise you will use a hybrid of the other two systems. If the operator is doing the inspecting, the feedback of any problems is instantaneous. The person who highlights the problem is the person who feeds back to the previous operator. Only one poor quality part should be produced before the problem is highlighted.

You might then say that poka-yoke is 100% inspection and that this is expensive and time consuming. Wrong. The beauty of the system is that components and processes are designed to alert the operator to poor quality without the need for that operator's involvement, with the result that inspection is not required on the good parts.

If you inspect a good part, that is a waste of resources. Why inspect it if it is good? With poka-yoke devices in place, poor parts are automatically flagged, so operators can work away sure in the knowledge that they are producing what they should be producing. There are checks that have to be carried out, but these are to the system itself – for instance each poka-yoke station may have a poor quality standard component from the previous station that is used at the start and end of every shift to ensure that the system is operating in the designed manner. If it is poor quality then the station being tested will not operate.

Poka-yoke in industry has generally become to be accepted as preventing bad components from moving through the process line. However, there are a number of different areas that poka-yoke is used in, some of which are mentioned below.

The main benefits of this system are obvious:

1. less scrap and rework
2. greater quality control
3. safety issues can be addressed
4. machinery can be protected.

Let us look at these with a few examples thrown in:

Less scrap and rework

What is the point of carrying out an operation if you have to eventually rework or scrap the component because earlier operations were either missed out or completed incorrectly? There isn't one.

A few simple examples:

- The placing of a limit switch into an automated production line for car door internal panels. If a section of the panel was required to be removed in order that a stereo speaker could be fitted, then the limit switch would not be made if the hole was there. If the hole was missing, the switch would be made, thereby letting the line know that an operation had been missed out.

- When I was sending off a lot of CVs after graduating, I was forever ending up with the last letter addressed to one firm and the last envelope addressed to another. After doing this a number of times, I started purchasing window envelopes, where the address on the letter also acted as the address for the envelope.
- If toppings are made onto food products, a check weigh and automatic reject system will highlight that the operation has either been missed out or that the ingredients hopper is empty. Not a true form of poka-yoke but part-way there.

Greater Quality Control

Poka Yoke ensures that you are not passing poor quality parts onto your customers.

- Moving components. If a number of tubes with an internal thread, machined to a minimum depth, have to be moved between work areas or stations, a transfer frame could be made up where the tubes were fastened to it by screwing them to bolts. If the tubes fall off, the thread is bad. If they don't screw in, they haven't been threaded. If they screw in and there is a gap between tube and frame, the thread is not deep enough.
- Consider mounting quality gauges into the fixtures of CNC machines. This will allow go/no go checks to be carried out as the component moves around the cell.
- A number of drilling or milling operations carried out on a component within a production cell. The second station may have a dowel pin fastened somewhere that would locate into a hole drilled at the first station. If the component didn't fit into station number 2 you would immediately know that the hole had not been drilled at station 1.

Safety issues

- Interlock systems on machinery ensure that the machine is only capable of working if the guards and screening are in place, stopping the operators from trapping themselves in moving parts. Some machines require the safety systems to be 'locked on'. If operators wish to enter the guarded area, as long as they have the key with them, the machine cannot be switched on.

- You may remember from a few years ago, and indeed it may be carried out still, that on certain sections of the British rail system where there is only a single section of track, a train can not start down the track unless they have a marker. As there is only one marker, only one train can travel at a time. The timetable obviously has to ensure that two trains do not travel in the same direction consecutively, but rather they have to alternate, therefore the system ensures that in remote upland areas there is a reduced chance of a collision.
- Fast food chains colour code their cleaning materials to match their décor. Therefore all chemicals in containers coloured red can only be used in areas that are red, materials that are yellow can only be used in yellow areas etc. This allows toilet cleaning equipment to be kept separate from food hygiene chemicals and general table-top cleaners.
- If you are rough cutting prior to precision cutting on lathe or CNC stations, then you may want to ensure that the rough cut has actually been completed otherwise there is a risk that as the smooth cut tool moves in it will shatter on the material that hasn't been removed.

Machinery Protection

- It wasn't until I worked as a designer for a petrol pump manufacturer that I noticed that diesel pump nozzles are bigger than leaded petrol nozzles, which in turn are bigger than unleaded nozzles. The car fuel tank inlet pipes are similarly designed. You cannot put diesel into a car designed for petrol, or leaded into an un-leaded car.
- Controlling the size of materials. If a piece of plant is capable of handling materials up to a certain size only, the placing of mesh over the hopper or infeed section would ensure that nothing over a specific set of dimensions would pass through.

These are all very simple ideas. However, in the main, you will want to be concentrating on ideas that stop poor quality components from progressing down the production line and eventually leaving site.

As each poka-yoke solution is to a certain extent workstation specific, all that I can give you here is an understanding that such a technique is available, and the basic overview.

The main aspect is the generation of innovative ideas that suit your specific needs.

CEDAC – Problem Solving Techniques

CEDAC is only a single part of the problem solving technique that over time has lent its name to the overall philosophy.

CEDAC therefore is a process for solving problems. The 'CED' part of the name refers to a 'Cause and Effect Diagram', a basic plan, if you like, of the problems encountered and the interaction between them. The 'AC' refers to 'Added Cards', highlighters of possible solutions and the state of play of those solutions.

So what is the overall philosophy ?

This section aims to set out a few fundamentals for problem solving within the workplace.

Firstly, a definition:

A problem occurs when what is happening differs from what *should* be happening.

With the use of a few simple bits of paperwork, we can identify the main problems and from there implement solutions to eliminate these problems.

The sheets that we will be using are:

- Problem Listing and Pareto
- Time Observation
- Flow Diagram
- Cause and Effect Diagram
- ... and '5 Whys ?' will also be covered.

There are ten steps towards Problem Solving:

1. Determine what the problem is
2. Describe the Problem
3. Objective Statement – Conditions and Date
4. Create Flow chart for process
5. Pinpoint external relationships
6. Introduce temporary solutions if desired
7. Determine causes

8. Decide on and implement solutions
9. Monitor effects
10. Standardise procedures

1. Determine What the Problem is

The first step has already been covered in the Tools for the Job section, under the Pareto Analysis section. There is no need to go over it again, that is why it is in a separate section, however read it once more so it is fresh in your mind.

Have a look at a completed sheet for this section (see page overleaf).

2. Describe the Problem

Once the problems have been highlighted, placed in order of importance and one or two have been selected for analysis, the problem should be written down.

- The description should be clear, concise and specific.
- It should be simple, but have impact.
- It should be able to be understood by anyone.
- Do not use the word ...Why

Why it is happening is not something that we want to know at this stage. We don't yet have enough information to decide on the reasons, and to go into the exercise with pre-determined answers will not benefit anyone.

Common Errors in the description

Solving the problem in the statement:

Do not say – *'We need a new lathe template.'*

Say – *'There is a problem with the accuracy of the head profile'*

Being too general in the statement:

Do not say – *'The cell has a 15% reject rate.'*

Say – *'The Head Profile trim operation in the Forming cell causes a 6.5% reject rate when running the M36x150 cap screw.'*

Being too vague in the statement:

Do not say – *'We've had complaints about head concentricity.'*

Say – *'5% of our customers have reported head eccentricity about the shank on the M36x150 cap screws'*

Sheet type - Kaizen, Single Task, Repetitive Task, Combination Sheet, Location, Problem Listing and Pareto, Time Observation

Location: *Forming cell* | Observer: | Process: *Form, cut, trim, thread*

Date: *November 2003* | Observation: | Component: *M36x150 Cap*

Time:

Number	Concerns, measured as individuals				5th	6th	7th	8th	9th	10	20	30	40	50		Tot
1	Poor head profile				IIIII I	IIIII IIIII I	IIIII III	IIIII II	IIIII III							40
2	Shank too long				III	II	I	I	III							10
3	Shank too short					II	I	II								5
4	Head not concentric about the shank						IIII	I								5
5	Bad thread at head end				IIIII	IIIII	IIIII									15
				Total	14	20	19	11	11							75

If you get your problems clearly laid out here it will keep you on the straight and narrow, focused about the main area of concern and you will not spend time and resources trailing off to try and solve other problems.

3. Objective Statement – Conditions and Date

If we take our Problem Description as being ...

'The Head Profile trim operation in the Forming cell has a 6.5% reject rate when running the M36x150 cap screw.'

... then our Objective Statement will be:

'Reduce the defects on the head profile trimming operation in the Forming cell for M36x150 cap screws from 6.5% to 0.5% by [date], using the Problem Listing and Pareto Sheet as our measurement.'

(If you state 0%, this means 0%, not 0.1% or 0.0001%. 0% is very specific.)

The Objective Statement should make good use of words such as Reduce, Achieve, Increase. Any word in fact that gives a strong and powerful image to what we are trying to do. Okay, so I'm trying to make it more dynamic and exciting, but a bit of enthusiasm never went amiss.

Set a target date. Be specific. (The target date should be the last day of the event.)

One vitally important thing – detail *what* is going to be measured, *how* it will be measured and *how often* it will be measured. If there are no hard and fast data, how will you know what you have achieved? Use the same measuring method that highlighted the problem in the first place, hence the inclusion in the Objective Statement of 'using the Problem Listing and Pareto Sheet as our measurement.'

To clearly see if the exercise is on course, a Time Observation Chart should be constructed. This is used in conjunction with the Problem Listing and Pareto sheet. Whereas the Pareto Graph covers all problems in a short period of time, the Time Observation Chart covers only the Objective Statement problem over the time period specified, this usually being the duration of the exercise. As with the Pareto it is mainly used as a visual aid.

Additional Notes

- The Dates generally cover the duration of the exercise and the time periods used should be equal.

- The target line is plotted, starting with the present situation in the upper row and the desired situation in the bottom row. A line is then drawn between the two.
- From here the frequencies are plotted, giving a simple indicator of how the improvements are faring.
- The actual % figure should be given for an accurate working number.
- The observer should initial the sheet in case of queries, and this would generally be the operator assigned to the project team who is running the cell on a day-to-day basis.

Eventually, the Time Observation Chart should look like the following:

Sheet type - Kaizen, Single Task, Repetitive Task, Combination Sheet, Location, Problem Listing and Pareto, Time Observation

Location: Forming cell | Observer: As shown | Process: Form, ~~cut, trim,~~ thread

Date: As shown | Observation: As shown | Component: M36x150 caps

Time: As shown

Date & time	Comments	Obs	% per shift		% plotting (1–12)
3/11 day shift	Day one, no significant change to defect rate	WSR	6.5		
3/11 day shift	Implementation of 1st off ideas	WSR	4.95		
3/11 day shift	Trials of ideas carried out. No significant production figures	CJB			
3/11 day shift	New fixture fitted and guide rails reworked	WSR	2.5		
3/11 day shift	Remaining ideas all implemented	WSR	0.5		

Objective - Reduce the defects on the head profile trimming operation in Forming cell for M36x150 cap screws from 6.5% to 0.5% by 7/11/200-

4. Create Flow chart for process

As with the Pareto analysis, this was covered in the 'Tools for the Job' section, so once again go back and refresh your memory.

It is important to create an Actual and an Ideal flow chart, paying particular attention to the differences between them.

Remember, a problem occurs when what should be happening differs from what is happening, and these flow charts will show at a glance where the main areas of deviation occur.

5. Pinpoint External Relationships

One of the main advantages of the Flow Chart is that it lets the team see the process or operation from an overall perspective, with each input and element broken down to its basic parts. From this, all external influences on the system can be seen and documented.

By external influences, we mean items such as conveyors or chutes that may damage a component, storage or handling trays that may introduce dirt or oil to the system, surfaces that may produce rapid cooling resulting in distortion, in effect the 1001 reasons that can come into play.

Through looking at the external influences, the team can decide on whether these have any part to play in the forming of the problem. This is decided through simple detective work, asking questions such as:

Are the parts damaged before they reach the work area?
Is the component clean before being placed on the transfer system?
Will the component distort on a different surface?

If each external influence can be easily seen, a trace on these influences is easier to follow.

Each external influence can be tackled by a member or pair from the team rather than the entire team, leading to a mass of information on the state of the system being obtained in a short time.

If initial problem areas are highlighted in this instance, the team can then focus their full attention on the swift and accurate solving of the problem.

6. Introduce temporary solutions if desired

Remember – **Temporary Solutions**

This stage is only really used if the team has been put together in a short time period to address the problems that are having a major impact on production, resulting in supply issues, large amounts of poor quality or rework or some other time critical issue. It is considered to be a stop-gap solution and not usually associated with the longer-term, planned approach. In most factories, this would be termed 'fire fighting'.

This should only be carried out if the customer is going to be directly affected, be it from poor quality, failure to meet order requirements and the like.

By 'temporary' we mean the likes of 100% inspection, or even 200% inspection if it is deemed necessary. And in most factories, the general attitude would be – 'that's the problem solved'. It isn't. Have another read through the 5 Whys section if you also take this approach and have this attitude.

The Problem Solving doesn't stop here. If it does, then the team are not stopping the fires from being lit, they are merely fire-fighting.

If components are being scratched, then run thick tape down the transfer rails. Replace metal trays with plastic ones. Use individual compartments for each component instead of placing 24 haphazardly into a box.

Make good use of string and Sellotape. If it looks bad, all the better, it will push you to make a good job if it turns out to be permanent. If it is just a quick fix solution, even a trial, don't worry about aesthetics. They won't be there for long.

7. Determine causes

The main aspects of this stage are CEDAC and the 5 Whys? Once again, refer to the 5 Whys? section in the Tool Box for a refresher.

A Cause and Effect Diagram with Added Cards, CEDAC is also sometimes referred to as a fish bone diagram, herring bone diagram or as an Ishikawa diagram, the last more in keeping with the recurring Japanese theme.

So what does a CEDAC diagram look like? The following shows the basic layout of the diagram, this example showing the set-up for a production area.

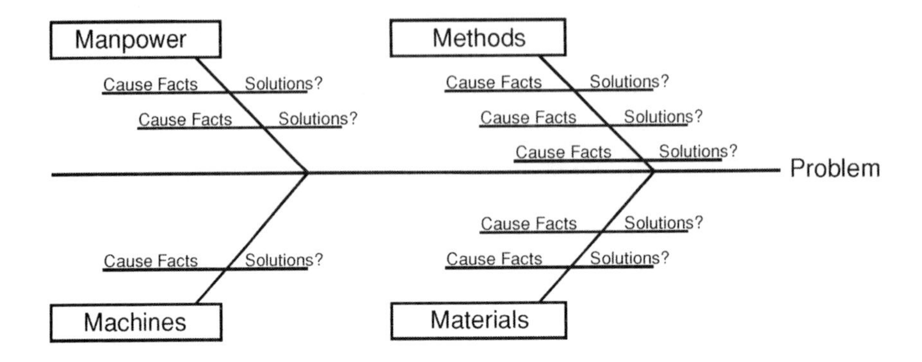

The CEDAC shows the four areas of Cause, with the Effect being the problem. The Added Cards detail the 'cause facts' surrounding the causes and any ideas (solutions) that can be tried out to eliminate the problem.

Four Causes for Production	Manpower, Methods, Machines, Materials
Four Causes for Administration	Policies, Procedures, People, Plant

How is it Constructed ?

Simply start off with the fishbone diagram shown above, entering the four relevant causes for the problem area, either production or administration, and the effect. The effect is what we encountered in section 2, the description of the problem.

When drawing the diagram it should be remembered that the final CEDAC will be very big. Using a whole large whiteboard or a few sheets of A3 or A2 paper taped together will not usually be enough. Some diagrams that I have worked with are over thirty feet long. The best solution is to steal a roll of paper from the AutoCad plotters, as these can be up to four feet across and very long. Even then it may be necessary to use two levels of paper. As you gain experience of CEDAC, a better judgement from an early stage will help in this situation.

The diagram must be clearly visible to every team member from within the exercise room.

Where do the Added Cards come from?

The Added Cards highlight areas that the team thinks may be responsible for the poor quality components. We call them 'facts' at present even though they are really only suggestions. The reasoning is that if we assume they are contributing, then we will give each one an equal shout rather than leaving it behind when a major breakthrough is achieved. We want to consider everything, so don't leave anything behind.

The causes of the problems are derived through experience, discussion, agreement, good engineering skills and common sense. The team should brainstorm the four sections of the diagram, feeding back from the problem to the possible causes.

There is also the 5 Whys section to follow up. You should have re-read it before you started reading through this section. Make good use of it. It will solve the majority of your problems.

If we look at our earlier problem, 'The Head Profile trim operation in the Forming cell causes a 6.5% reject rate when running the M36x150 cap screw', then we would consider possibly the following:

Manpower

- Is the component being placed correctly into the collet?
- Has the operator had enough of the required training?
- Are the correct quality procedures being followed?
- Are there poka-yoke systems being bypassed?

Methods

- Should the operations be carried out in a different order?
- Is uneven metal cooling prior to the operation playing any significant part?
- Is the supply of components regular? (Can this effect m/c running speeds, temperature etc.?)
- Is the state of the component supply consistent? Temperature, length.

Machines

- Is the correct collet fitted?
- Is the collet fitted correctly?
- Is there an issue with shaft wear?
- Is the spindle concentric?

- Is there always a constant drive?
- Is the machine base capable of producing the tolerances necessary?

Materials

- Are we using the correctly specified metal?
- Are the raw components to the required specification?
- Are there inclusions/impurities in the metal?

Some of these questions may be fitted into more than one of the categories, it really doesn't matter as long as they are included somewhere. The bonus of the diagram being large is that if one possible cause falls into another section then it is easily found.

Place Added Cards with the Cause Facts onto the diagram

The facts on these cards are the facts that we have just looked at, derived for each of the four causes. These fact cards should be red Post-it notes. Red is traditionally associated with 'danger'. Post-it notes make it easy for the cards to be moved or edited.

- When filling in the fact cards, use specific details, not broad generalisations. Try and pinpoint what you are considering rather than just hinting at. For example, make the distinction between:
  • Is the correct collet fitted? ... and • Is the collet fitted correctly?
- A few well chosen words are enough to convey an entire idea.
- Each fact card should contain only one idea.
- Each fact card is a specific part of the solution process, so don't mix and match.
- There has to be traceability and ownership of the fact cards so date them and assign them to a team member or members to analyse the possible cause. Initial the cards with the members names.
- Above all, make the fact cards understandable to anyone. This means not just clear and concise facts, but also literate and readable.

The team should consider the following when filling in the fact cards:

- Causes
- Facts
- Observations

- Perceptions
- Opinions
- Questions
- Obstacles

Ask the following questions:

Who
... is it affecting?
... does it?
... should do it?
... else can do it?
... else should do it?

What
... are the consequences?
... is being done?
... should be done?
... else can be done?
... else should be done?

Where/When/How
... is it done?
... should it be done?
... else is it done?
... else should it be done?

Why
... do they do it?
... do they do it there?
... do they do it that way?

Where do the Solution Cards come from?

Once all possible causes contributing to the problem have been considered, it is only then that the solutions can be addressed.

The work that has gone before this stage, namely filling in all of the sheets and charts, will have given the team an understanding of what the problem is, the possible causes and how the process works. They will be able to contribute more to the solution if they know the basic facts.

Solution cards should be green Post-it notes, green being associated with 'go'. Again, Post-it notes make the diagram easily edited.

The basic principles for filling these in are the same. Namely clear, concise and understandable by anyone.

Each of the solutions will have been arrived at through the ideas put forward by the team member or members assigned to analyse the corresponding Fact Card. However, everyone has a say. If the solution is thought by the team as a whole to be irrelevant or incomplete, then it should be changed.

The solution cards should express the following:

- suggestions
- recommendations
- counter-measures
- corrective ideas
- improvement ideas.

Consider the following actions with regards to the solution cards:

- revise them
- expand on them
- reduce them
- substitute them
- review them
- combine them
- steal them from other events/teams.

... and:

- be creative, think of strange but viable solutions
- don't be afraid of failure
- consider alternative solutions – don't settle for the first one you come across
- give everyone an equal say
- don't be afraid to make mistakes.

However, consider also the following:

- Who will be affected by your actions?
- What will happen if the actions that you put into place fail? (This should only cause problems with big suggestions.)
- Who will be affected by any failures? (That is an important one: customers, suppliers?)
- Advance once everyone is satisfied with the solutions put forward.

Benefits of the Diagram?

- ☑ It involves everyone. Don't be afraid to involve other sections of the workplace.
- ☑ Very visual, therefore open to non-team members' views and opinions.
- ☑ Considers all aspects that can contribute to the problem. It shows an

overall picture of causes and eliminates the jumping to conclusions or gut feelings.

☑ Keeps track of progress and effects in a clear manner.

☑ The use of Post-it notes allows quick and easy re-arranging as required as the board expands.

☑ The use of clearly written and easily understood cards keeps everyone abreast of the problems and solutions.

☑ It is flexible. We have specified a fishbone shape here but the CEDAC can be any shape the team wishes, so long as it is easily understood.

Brief summary on the Diagram

1. Decide on the shape
2. Enter causes: Production or Administrative?
3. Introduce Cause and Effect cards
4. Introduce Solution Cards
5. (Next section) Implement Solutions

Remember – CEDAC involves everyone in the search for the solution, not just the team members. As we have seen, the CEDAC looks at every aspect of the problem area and asks questions about every input to this area. And who knows the problem area and its suppliers better than anyone else? The workforce. So don't limit the scope of the team's solutions purely to the team itself. There will obviously be a very strong workforce representation on the team, but they may not know all aspects of the supply (previous) and customer (next) processes, therefore do not be afraid to involve the experience and expertise of other people.

Here is a small example, designed around the problem of poor tasting tea:

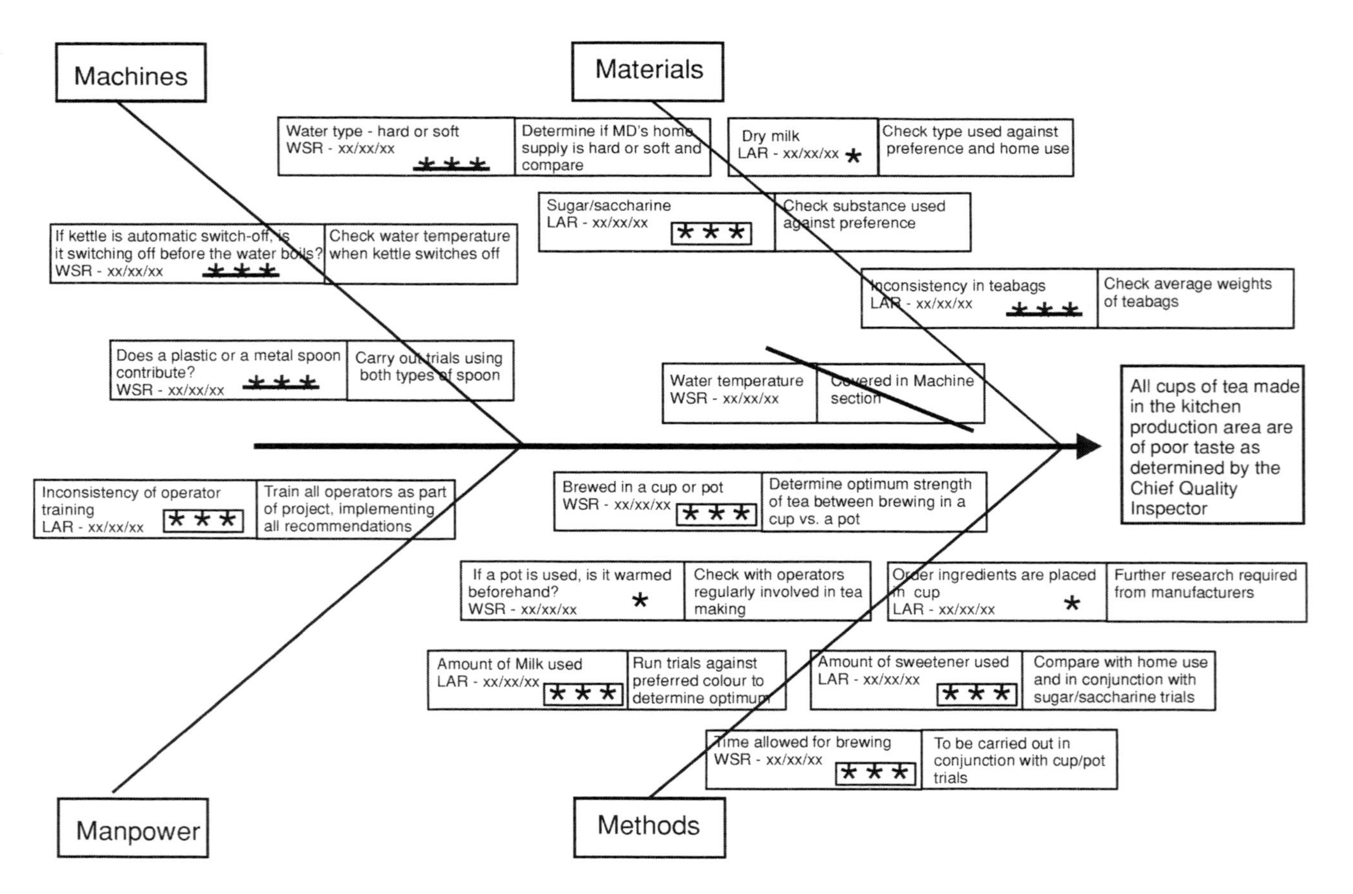
Machines
Materials
Water type - hard or soft WSR - xx/xx/xx
Determine if MD's home supply is hard or soft and compare
Dry milk LAR - xx/xx/xx
Check type used against preference and home use
Sugar/saccharine LAR - xx/xx/xx
Check substance used against preference
If kettle is automatic switch-off, is it switching off before the water boils? WSR - xx/xx/xx
Check water temperature when kettle switches off
Inconsistency in teabags LAR - xx/xx/xx
Check average weights of teabags
Does a plastic or a metal spoon contribute? WSR - xx/xx/xx
Carry out trials using both types of spoon
Water temperature WSR - xx/xx/xx
Covered in Machine section
All cups of tea made in the kitchen production area are of poor taste as determined by the Chief Quality Inspector
Inconsistency of operator training LAR - xx/xx/xx
Train all operators as part of project, implementing all recommendations
Brewed in a cup or pot WSR - xx/xx/xx
Determine optimum strength of tea between brewing in a cup vs. a pot
If a pot is used, is it warmed beforehand? WSR - xx/xx/xx
Check with operators regularly involved in tea making
Order ingredients are placed in cup LAR - xx/xx/xx
Further research required from manufacturers
Amount of Milk used LAR - xx/xx/xx
Run trials against preferred colour to determine optimum
Amount of sweetener used LAR - xx/xx/xx
Compare with home use and in conjunction with sugar/saccharine trials
Time allowed for brewing WSR - xx/xx/xx
To be carried out in conjunction with cup/pot trials
Manpower
Methods

8. Implement solutions

Initially you should take the same approach as you took with Stage 6. Don't go overboard with investment of time, money and effort. Make lots of good use of string and Sellotape, use the suck-it-and-see approach. If the solution works, good. Then you follow it through and implement whatever is necessary to provide a permanent fix. If it doesn't work, don't worry. You haven't spent major resources on it, but at least you tried to do something.

Keeping a track of Solutions, whether they work or not, is very important. This is where the Kaizen Monthly comes into play, in that it lets us know the state of play of proposals.

In addition, if the team members are working on different aspects of the problem, they need to know what the others are up to without calling everyone together for a formal review.

In order to keep a track of the progress, use a set of simple symbols:

*	**Of interest – the team has decided that this is worth following up**
**	**Preparation work is under way to try this out**
~~**~~	**The trial was rejected. Possibly another factor came into play or the early work carried out showed that it would be unfeasible. Explain the decision on the card**
***	**The suggestion is being tested. Let's see if it works.**
~~***~~	**The trial was completed however the results proved to be of no benefit. Explain why on the card.**
[***]	**The results were good and the trial solution will be made permanent**

These marks are added to the cards as the exercise progresses. You will notice that they can be added – the cards do not have to be re-written. I would suggest leaving the lower half of the cards free from writing in order that these symbols can be entered.

These can be placed on either of the cards.

As the team implements their ideas, it will be worth considering the following

- Is there a plan for large scale, permanent implementation of successful trials?

- Who will do what?
- Is there a time frame for the plans?
- Have you thought about the consequences of changing the system?
- Is there a contingency plan in case of failure?
- If there is a knock on effect to customers or suppliers, has it been thought through?

Some of these have been mentioned in other sections, but they are important.

9. Monitor effects

We have already mentioned that the long-term success or otherwise of the event will be judged through the use of the Problem Listing Sheet over a given time period. This sheet will form the basis of the information presented to the kaizen review team over the months. If the problem re-occurs, the team will be able to pick up on it within the frequency of the meetings. In the fullness of time, this monitoring will pass to the factory floor, with the operators and junior management being responsible for highlighting re-occurrence or increase of the problem.

Having done a good job in the event though, this problem should not re-occur.

In addition to this, good use should also be made during the event of the Problem/Time Chart. It will show if you are following the goals set by yourselves.

10. Standardise procedures

And finally, once you have carried out all of this good work, you want it to stay in place. Stage 9 will highlight if it starts to slip, but in order to help the new system stay where it was left by the team, then some form of standardisation must be written.

The section on Work Standardisation will cover aspects of this, as far as manual operations are concerned, through the use of the Combination Sheet, detailing the actions and the associated times (if relevant) that each action should take.

The section on 5S – specifically the last section on Sustaining the good work – will also provide some hints and tips.

In addition, if the team thinks that they are relevant, then a step-by-step procedure for operations may be created, detailing the condition and operation of certain aspects of the system, such as the amount of protective covering on guide rails, Teflon coating must be used on chutes, no paint to be used in certain areas etc.

And a quick recap of the main benefits

1. It solves your problems.
2. It involves a large number of people, therefore good for spreading the word.
3. A number of various tools are incorporated into the overall philosophy, providing a good grounding in kaizen philosophies.
4. It is very visual, making good use of graphs and charts, and therefore generates a lot of interest from those not directly involved.

Failure Mode and Effects Analysis – FMEA

FMEA is used to identify in a component what can go wrong, how it can go wrong and what can be done to stop it from going wrong – what the Failure Mode is and the Analysis of the Effects.

This then allows manufacturing procedures and techniques to be laid down and/or improved. As a result, better quality is achieved, customer satisfaction is improved and scrap levels are reduced.

If these are not good reasons for introducing FMEA, there are others such as statutory regulations, customer demands (particularly in sub-assembly components) and legal/warranty claims. In fact, all the reasons that you would associate with greater quality.

FMEA can be introduced either at the new product design stage, as a Design FMEA or a Production FMEA, or it can be used to tackle issues in an existing production plant. The same principles that we will cover can also be applied to the service sections of your business – accounts, stock ordering and so on.

There are many similarities between FMEA and CEDAC. However, CEDAC tends to be used in the solving of problems, FMEA used in the prevention of problems. That said, each is 90% interchangeable with the other. It is just that the way each system has been developed and grown that leads to the distinction above. It is advisable to be fully aware of the CEDAC section for pointers on Pareto and any other associated techniques.

Common or garden methods of analysing concerns may not be structured enough to identify failure modes and their effects, (too much reliance on gut feelings and the like). However, a more structured, professional approach works due to the following.

1. There may be too many failure modes to accurately identify through normal methods.
2. There is a workplace thought process that if we ignore it, it may go away. If it does go away, we do not know why, and it will come back at some point. A clearly documented investigation of the problem and designated corrective actions will eliminate this.

3. It looks at the specifics, not just the general situation.

There are two main ways in which FMEA can be tackled.

1. **The simple** – what can go wrong, how can it go wrong, what can we do?
2. **In depth** – as above, but with weighting attached.

There are similarities in the following sections, so read each of them.

The Simple

As an example in this section, we will be looking at the manufacture of a cup of tea. Our customer, the Chief Quality Inspector, wants us to provide:

'A cup of tea, milk, two sugars.'

We will assume that there are specifications regarding the actual physical amount of sugar, milk etc to be used in the process, as laid down in Specification Sheets and the like. We will look at a situation of Production FMEA.

We start by splitting the component down into the constituent parts and analysing each possible Failure Mode. In making a cup of tea, this may include the strength, temperature, sweetness, delivery and general manufacturing processes. Materials, manufacture and techniques if you like.

Each possible Failure Mode may occur due to a number of specific causes. These must all be considered. For instance, the final flavour may be affected by the strength of the tea, and the causes of the tea being too weak or too strong may be an incorrect tea bag, infusion time, amount of water used, temperature of water used and the amount of milk used. As with the use of a car in the TPM section, we are looking at the main areas as general individual sections before breaking these down further into specifics.

As you will see from the table below, each of these main sections has been designated a number, with subdivisions following for the specifics. (1., 1.1, 1.2, 2., 2.1 etc.) This eliminates any confusion when referencing each point.

The 'Action Points' shown should be obtained from a brainstorming session. At this stage, they are purely for discussion as there may be a debate between, say, fitting automatic dispensers or improving the manual process, and both items should be given equal consideration. This approach is very similar to the CEDAC chart. In this stage try and be as specific and accurate as possible – if you do not get it right here, you will not get it right further on. The experience and skill of the team will ensure that this happens. There must be an accurate understanding of the process.

Remember though that string and Sellotape will be sufficient to prove a point. (Refer also to sections 4 and 5 in the 'In Depth' section on the following pages.)

In addition, it may be worthwhile having quality paperwork (ISO, customer specs.) and suppliers specifications to hand, and possibly a supplier representative on the team to advise on their manufacturing processes and variables. As this is a Production FMEA, there will need to be considerable contact with the customer. I suggest that the Chief Quality Inspector does nothing for a day except sit in their office and drink tea.

You may want to number each of the action points to provide even better control over the system. However, I would suggest that these are left to the final sheet as this will be used in training new operators, quality checks etc.

There is also a 'Who' column to provide allocation of tasks.

This will be the main document that the team has to work with. It will act as a guide through the entire process, in a similar vein to the Kaizen Monthly only more component/area specific, and will act as a point of reference for your customers. (This does not mean to say that you do not use a Kaizen Monthly.) Especially in the automotive sector, the Original Equipment Manufacturers like to see documented FMEAs.

The team should have an accurate picture of the manufacturing process and the interactions of external forces. Go ahead and investigate possible causes of poor quality. Use the techniques learned from the CEDAC.

With the elimination or implementation of the action points, the quality and customer service of the organisation will improve.

All of the above will be seen on the following table:

Failure Mode and Effects Analysis

Component: Cup of tea   Part Number: TEA-2S-M   Customer: Chief Quality Inspector
FMEA Team: AA, BB, CC, DD, EE, FF   Date of exercise: xx/xx/xx

	Quality issue		Possible causes	Action points	Who
1.	Strength of tea	1.1	Incorrect teabag used	Check spec. sheets for type v.'s requirements before commencement of production.	AA
				To be included on an operator tick sheet.	BB
				Obtain quality assurances from supplier and monitor	AA
				Fit poka-yoke to ensure correct bag used	AA
		1.2	Infuse time	Fit automatic dunk system. (Must be fitted with ability to differentiate by product type)	AA
				Provide timer/alarm system for operator.	CC
		1.3	Volume of water used	Fit automatic dosing and dispensing system	EE
		1.4	Temperature of water used	Fit second automatic thermocouple and signal device to boiling equipment	DD
				Introduce daily operator manual check on temperature	DD
				Introduce weekly TPM checks	DD
				Ensure container fabric wrt varying temperature dissipation is constant. (One container only envisaged, however replacements to be considered)	AA
		1.5	Variations in the milk	Check proposed methods of milk dispersal.	FF
				Reconcile measuring devices with specifications. (milk to be dispersed with an audited container)	AA
				Fit automatic dispersal system.	BB
				To be dispersed at a set temperature	CC
				A specific type to be used only - full fat, semi-skimmed or fully-skimmed	CC
				Milk used to be very date specific fresh delivery on day of use	AA
2	Temperature of tea (Must be >90°C)	2.1	See item 1.4 above See item 1.5 above 'Milk Temperature'		
3.	Varying sweetness	3.1	Incorrect amount of sugar used	Check proposed methods of sugar dispersal.	DD
				Reconcile measuring devices with specifications. ('2 sugars' to be dispersed with a single container, not 2 off 'single sugars')	DD
				Fit automatic dispersal system.	FF
		3.2	Varying quality of sugar used	Ensure that supplies are within specifications. Ask for supplier guarantee.	FF
				Introduce batch QA checks.	AA
4.	Stirring process	4.1	Technique used	Specifics to be laid down wrt :- stirring time, direction of stir, amount of rotations around the cup, material used in stirring device.	ALL

5	General	2	5.1	Container	Must be bone china for optimum taste - supplier guarantee required in case of replacement	AA
			5.2	Tea pot	Must be silver plated at the very least - silver standard to be considered. Pot to be pre-warmed - further investigation to be carried out for methods. Pot is allowed to be kept warm with the use of a tea-cosy, as long as item 2 is adhered to.	AA DD FF
			5.3	Stirring device (reference Also item 4 above)	As with teapot, stirring device must be to same material specifications	CC
6	Delivery	5	6.1	Delivery	Must be achieved within time span allowed to ensure that temperatrure remains above 90°C. Further analysis required on this. (Tea is NOT ALLOWED TO BE REHEATED DUE TO TASTE QUALITY ISSUES.)	DD
	ALL PERSONNEL NOTE: THE TASTING OF TEA AS PART OF THE QUALITY CHECKS IS STRICTLY FORBIDDEN THIS WILL BE DEEMED A SACKABLE OFFENCE					

In Depth

This may be required and more suitable when there is a specific quality complaint or huge cost implications, for instance, automotive recall or food contamination.

The more in-depth approach looks at a weighting system applied to the problem and follows this up with a number of actions:

1. Analyse the three main factors:
    - the severity of a fault occurring
    - the risk (chances) of the fault occurring
    - the chances of not detecting the problem.
2. Provide these factors with a numerical rating.
3. Calculate the overall numerical rating for each Failure Mode.

The points 4 and 5 are also relevant to the 'Simple' section shown before.

4. Decide on action points to minimise or eliminate the three main factors.
5. Use the Problem Listing Sheet paperwork as a measure for improvement and reassurance for your customers.

1. Three main factors

The severity of the fault occurring

This covers what will happen if the fault occurs. If too much milk is included, then not only is the cup of tea ruined but the Quality Inspectors tea break will be ruined also. This is severe. Rework is required. If only 1½ sugars are included instead of 2, then the tea is still drinkable – however it is an inconvenience. This is not quite as severe a problem.

The risk of the fault occurring

(Either in service or in manufacturing, depending on your product) If there are ten different flavours of tea bag, all intermixed in a large storage jar and only identified by the smell, then there is a high risk that a fault will occur in the process. If only one type of sugar is used, white granulated, then the risk of using the incorrect sugar is minimal.

The chances of not detecting the problem

If the milk is not put into the tea then this will easily be identified through visual inspection as the cup moves through the process – the colour of the tea will be enough to identify it as incorrect, if sufficient operator training has occurred. The chances of not identifying the problem are small. If no sugar is included then this is very difficult to detect until the tea is tested. By this time it is already with the customer.

We will construct a table to take into account all of these issues, using the same criteria in the previous example.

The ranking system that we use will be:

Severity

1 Not severe if problem occurs
5 Very severe if problem occurs

Risk of Problem Occurring

1 Low risk of problem occurring
5 High risk of problem occurring

Chances of Identifying Problem

1 Easily identified if problem occurs
5 Very difficult to identify

It is up to you to decide what goes in between.

It can be seen that the Severity mark is for the overall Failure Mode whilst the other marks are for each possible cause.

Failure Mode and Effects Analysis

Component: Cup of tea   Part Number: TEA-2S-M   Customer: Chief Quality Inspector
FMEA Team: AA, BB, CC, DD, EE, FF   Date of exercise: xx/xx/xx

	Quality issue	Severity		Possible causes	Risk	Chances	Total	Action points	Who
1	Quality of tea	2	1.1	Incorrect teabag used	3	5	30	Check spec. sheets for type v.'s requirements before commencement of production. To be included on an operator tick sheet. Obtain quality assurances from supplier and monitor Fit poka-yoke to ensure correct bag used	AA BB AA AA
			1.2	Infuse time	3	5	30	Fit automatic dunk system. (Must be fitted with ability to differentiate by product type) Provide timer/alarm system for operator.	AA
			.3	Volume of water used	2	2	8	Fit automatic dosing and dispensing system	CC
			1.4	Temperature of water used	2	5	20	Fit second automatic thermocouple and signal device to boiling equipment Introduce daily operator manual check on temperature Introduce weekly TPM checks Ensure container fabric wrt varying temperature dissipation is constant. (One container only envisaged, however replacements to be considered)	EE DD DD DD AA
			1.5	Variations in the milk	2	2	8 **<u>96</u>**	Check proposed methods of milk dispersal. Reconcile measuring devices with specifications. (milk to be dispersed with an audited container) Fit automatic dispersal system. To be dispersed at a set temperature A specific type to be used only - full fat, semi-skimmed or fully-skimmed Milk used to be very date specific fresh delivery on day of use	 FF AA BB CC CC
2	Temperature of Tea (Must be >90°)	4	2.1	See item 1.4 above See item 1.5 above 'Milk temperature'	2 2	5 2	40 16 **<u>56</u>**		AA
3	Varying sweet-ness	2	3.1	Incorrect amount of sugar used	2	5	20	Check proposed methods of sugar dispersal. Reconcile measuring devices with specifications. ('2 sugars' to be dispersed with a single container, not 2 off 'single sugars') Fit automatic dispersal system.	DD DD FF
			3.2	Varying quality of sugar used	1	5	10 **<u>30</u>**	Ensure that supplies are within specifications. Ask for supplier guarantee. Introduce batch QA checks.	FF AA
4	Stirring process	1	4.1	Technique used	1	1	1 **<u>1</u>**	Specifics to be laid down wrt :- stirring time, direction of stir, amount of rotations around the cup, material used in stirring device.	ALL

5	General	2	5.1	Container	1	3	6	Must be bone china for optimum taste - supplier guarantee required in case of replacement	AA
			5.2	Tea pot	1	3	6	Must be silver plated at the very least - silver standard to be considered. Pot to be pre-warmed - further investigation to be carried out for methods. Pot is allowed to be kept warm with the use of a tea-cosy, as long as item 2 is adhered to.	AA DD FF
			5.3	Stirring device (reference Also item 4 above)	4	5	40 **52**	As with teapot, stirring device must be to same material specifications	CC
6	Delivery	5	6.1	Delivery	1	1	5 5	Must be achieved within time span allowed to ensure that temperatrure remains above 90°C. Further analysis required on this. (Tea is NOT ALLOWED TO BE REHEATED DUE TO TASTE QUALITY ISSUES.)	DD

ALL PERSONNEL NOTE - THE TASTING OF TEA AS PART OF THE QUALITY CONTROL CHECKS IS STRICTLY FORBIDDEN. THIS WILL BE DEEMED A SACKABLE OFFENCE.

2. Provide these factors with a numerical rating (as already shown)

The numerical rating for each concern is obtained by multiplying the Severity figure for the Failure Mode with each of the Risk and Chance figures.

To talk you through a few of the above:

- Taking 1.1 above – Strength of Tea showed a severity figure of 2. The tea will still be drinkable within a huge specification target. The only concerns that may occur here are that either no tea bag was used or more than one tea bag was used.

  The risk of the wrong tea bag was felt to be medium, so it was given a three. There were one or two concerns noted on the action sheet, so the group thought that there was a definite room for improvement.

  The chances of knowing whether the tea was within specified strength or not were extremely slim, and would not be discovered until the tea was being tasted by the customer. All inspection is visual, so a weight of 5 was put on this.

  The total figure then was 30.

- Item 4.1 – the stirring process. If the tea was not stirred, this should not be taken as a severe problem, more of an inconvenience. (The Chief Quality Inspector has been known to stir his tea with a pencil – however, this is a customer-only operation and is not allowed during manufacture)

  A mark of 1 was felt to be sufficient. Likewise the risk of the tea not being stirred was felt to be slim also as it is common practice to stir all cups whether required of not. Another 1.

  The process of making the tea allows the operator to know immediately if the tea has been stirred or not through simply looking at the surface of the tea in the cup. If it is moving in a circular motion, then he knows that the tea has been stirred within a recent timespan. Another 1.

  This gives a total of 1.

- 6.1 – Delivery of the Tea. If the tea is not ready for the Chief Quality Inspector when he is at his tea break, this is a very severe state of affairs, hence the figure of 5.

  However, the risks of this happening are slim given the nature of production and the culture within the organisation. Marked as 1.

Quality inspection wise, it is easy to see if there is a problem – there is a cup of tea or there is not a cup of tea. Again, 1.

Total of 5.

3. Calculate the overall numerical rating for each Failure Mode

These numerical ratings calculated above are totalled to provide an overall figure for each Failure Mode. (Bold and Underlined in the chart.) Very simple.

The total figures for each section will help to identify where the main thrust of improvements or manufacturing process investigation are required. As with the Pareto analysis that we discussed in the CEDAC section, it is not always the highest score that takes precedent – it may be better to handle a few low scoring items and eliminate them at an early stage.

It will also be seen that at this stage you may have a failure mode with a very low numeric total but it may contain one aspect that is exceedingly high. (Example 5.3 in the table). Do you want to target this specific point rather than the entire Failure Mode?

It is important that the weighting system is completed before the Action Points are discussed. This allows the total for each possible Failure Mode to be calculated and resources allocated accordingly.

4. Decide on Action Points to minimise or eliminate the three main factors

As with most other sections in this book, there are actions to be completed. The weighting figures applied are not so relevant here – there is a problem that you need to fix. It doesn't matter if it is a big or a small problem, it is a problem, so start coming up with solutions. Brainstorming. Use the skills of the team. As before, do not put all of the work onto one individual or department, remember that you are a team.

Again, item 5.3 – the tea can be stirred by any number of different spoons so you may wish to ban all spoons from site with the exception of silver plated, quality controlled and documented spoons, contained within specific areas of the plant.

Do not be too specific at this moment in time. Technical drawings of ideas are not required. Make good use of Sellotape and string.

5. Use the paperwork as a measure for improvement and reassurance for your customers.

After the action points have been accomplished or eliminated, the team should re-write the FMEA sheet to include just those action points that are being implemented and to remove the 'Who' column. This will be the master FMEA document for this production area. (The working sheets, created during the exercise, should be kept for future reference.)

As usual, this document should be easily accessible by all production personnel so they know why they are doing the things that they do. It should form the basis of manufacturing procedures as well as becoming a part of the training programme that is carried out by new personnel about to begin working in this area.

Implementation into TPM and machine capability checks should also be carried through.

Any changes in the future must be taken in conjunction with this document:

- quality checks
- manufacturing process changes
- modifications to the component
- changes of material
- handling of components.

What is meant by Work Standardisation?

Standardisation is a set of rules – not guidelines – the purpose of which are to maintain the most efficient method of production with a minimum of labour and WIP. Note that there is a difference between Work Standardisation and Standards. (WS, for short, is more commonly known to the older amongst us as Time and Motion Study.) WS is the overall study of what is happening. Standards are put in place once the WS exercise has been completed to ensure that what we want to happen does happen.

One problem that you will encounter with this initially is that people say:

'You're trying to make me work harder.'

We say:

'No. We're trying to get you to make more parts, more easily.'

The 'Work Smarter, not Harder' ethos.

Do you remember this?

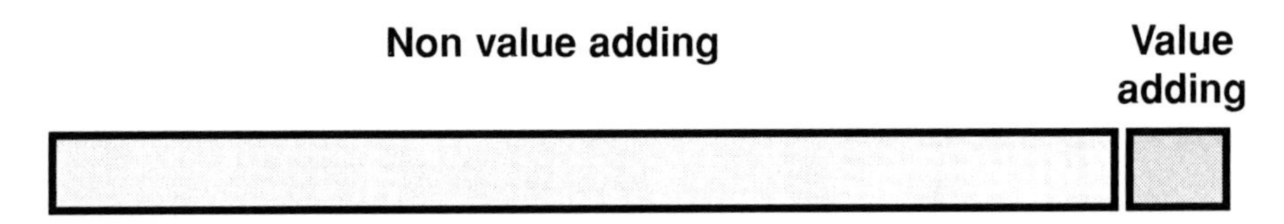

This is the 95% to 5% box, showing the ratio between Non Value Added and Value Added actions that are carried out in a typical factory. This is the reason that we require WS, to reduce the 95% part of the above. And even though you may think that you run a tight ship, you will be surprised at just how much waste there is in your operations.

So, how do we go about achieving Work Standardisation? There are a number of steps that should be followed as part of the basic outline and a few bits and pieces of paper:

- TAKT Time calculations
- Consider the work area.
- Study the work, using:

    - Repetitive Task Observation Sheet
    - Combination Sheet
    - Location Sheet
    - Problem Listing and Pareto
- Then – implement the ideas

TAKT Time

We have already had a look at takt time in the 'Tools' section, so if you would like to recap on this it will come in handy.

Consider the work area

In order to produce a component, we string together processes and operations:

Process The sequences involved in changing material
Operation Actions performed on the material

The process is made up of a number of operations, and as such we must evaluate the best method of integrating operations within the process, and following on from there the best method of integrating the process within the factory. Almost always, the best way to integrate is through Cellular Manufacturing, also known as One Piece Flow. Why is this best? Read on.

Traditional Factory Layout

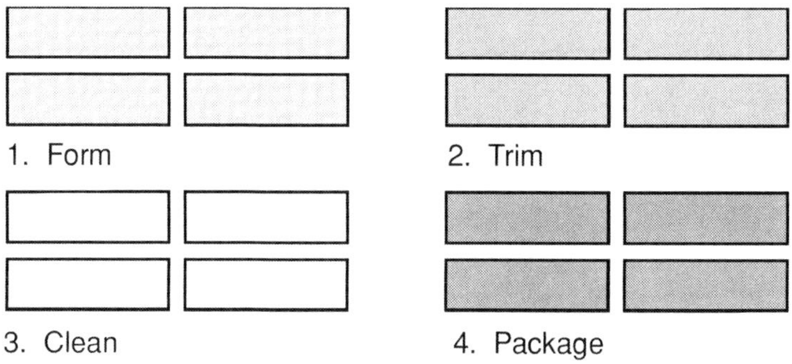

1. Form
2. Trim
3. Clean
4. Package

Each operation is carried out in a separate area of the factory. Once a predetermined batch size is reached, then the components are moved onto the next operation. This produces waste of:

- time
- movement 1 – parts
- stock
- production

In addition to this, paperwork is required to keep track of the components as they move around the factory, storage space is required and quality can be affected by future operations using the wrong components, components that are damaged or past their use-by date, shop soiled or not required any more due to a number of reasons.

Cellular Factory Layout

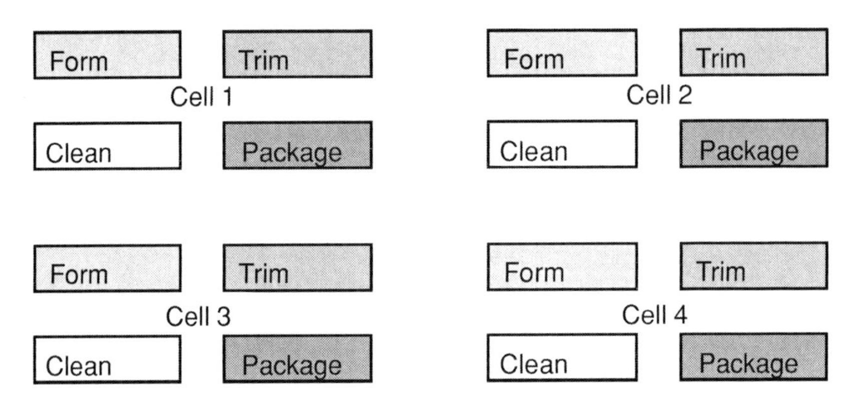

As can be seen, the factory is now broken up into four separate production cells as opposed to four process areas.

Let's have a look at the Advantages of this system

Less WIP – Once you have carried out work on a component, you have spent money on that component, whether value has been added or not. Less WIP, less money tied up. Less WIP, less storage costs. Less WIP, less administration required. Less WIP, less large scale defects.

Greater quality control – If, obviously, before you have finished reading this book, you had a major quality issue in the factory, would you rather have to scrap or rework two minutes worth of production or two months worth of production. Notice the lack of a question mark. It was a rhetorical question.

Reduced lead times – How can this be? A lead time is a lead time. Lead times are the length of time it takes between an order being placed and the product being delivered. You deliver to the customer, but the customer is the next person in the process, therefore they are not necessarily the people who are actually buying the product. The diagrams showing the difference between the traditional factory layout and the cellular layout, below, will help to explain this.

Less physical work – As you will see in a short period of time, the operator is not having to walk as far, move components as far or indeed move as many components as far.

Creates responsibility – I don't have to say anything about this other than it creates a feeling of ownership and pride in an area.

Less WIP

With batch production, you can't start the second operation until the first operation is complete. If it takes 20 minutes to complete each operation, it therefore takes 80 minutes to complete the process shown above, plus possible additional time to move between the various operational areas.

With cellular production, as soon as the first component completes the first operation, the second operation can begin.

For instance, imagine that you are asked to produce 20 components. If each cycle in the operation takes 1 minute, we will complete all four operations in 23 minutes as opposed to 80 minutes.

The following diagram will show this in better detail.

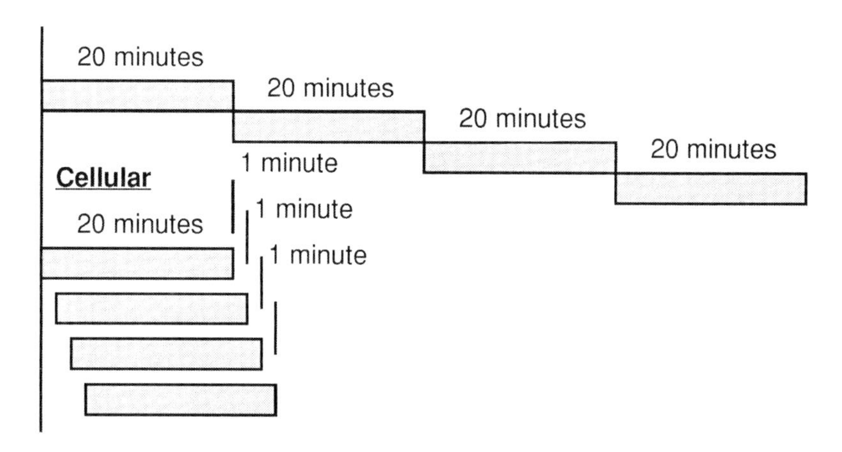

Batch production	- 80 minutes
1 Piece Flow	- 23 minutes

Even this very simple example shows the possible savings when a bit of thought is applied.

Greater Quality Control

This is obtained through three main points

1. The operator is responsible for the running of the cell, therefore it is down to him to ensure that quality is of a sufficiently high standard. This can be improved and made easier when Poka-Yoke is also introduced, reducing the need for intensive quality inspection.
2. The introduction of Work Standardisation details the number of components or time space between traditional quality checks, such as SPC, and will therefore act as a catalyst and reminder for quality.
3. If one operation is producing faulty components, then this is generally picked up on the next operation. This leads to a much smaller number of faulty components passing through before they are noticed, as opposed to a full batch production run. The main benefit of this is that one operator is involved in a number of different operations, therefore he will have a greater understanding of the process as a whole rather than one small section without any idea of what has gone before or will come after.

Reduced Lead Times

Look again at the simple example that I showed earlier.

Coupled to this, not only are you reducing the waiting times between operations but there is less time lost due to physical handling.

Creates Responsibility

Operators take greater care of a work area if they regard it as their own. By the very shape of cellular production areas a feeling of territory is introduced. (This will become evident in the quality, efficiency and cleanliness of the work area.)

Creating responsibility also creates a feeling of ownership. It is a two way relationship.

Operators will take pride in what they do.

Less Physical Work

With a greater understanding of the work area and the benefits thereafter, we tend to acquire a situation where machinery is situated much closer together, therefore a perfect opportunity arises to introduce automatic handling and transfer systems. These allow the operator more time to concentrate on the running of the production machinery without having to bother about loading hoppers and chutes. Note though that this is most efficient when creating a cell comprised of automatic machinery as opposed to manually operated machinery. Consider the following – conveyors, lifters, venturi pipes, bowl feeders.

So, I've tried to put the case for cellular, one-piece flow manufacturing in a few short pages, but I hope that it has whet your appetite enough for you to want to try it out.

What we want to be considering now is the analysis of the work in existing environments, whilst adding a few little pointers to the creation of further or entirely new areas.

Study the Work

With the aid of a few observation sheets the most efficient pattern for production can be arrived at.

The technique is to evaluate the actions that go into making up an operation, then the operations that make processes, calculate average times for all and use the information obtained to set down Work Standardisation procedures.

The sheets that we will be using are:

- Repetitive Task Observation Sheet
- Combination Sheet
- Location Sheet
- Problem Listing and Pareto

If considering the creation of a completely new cell area and not just the re-arranging of an existing area, then it is advisable to create a full scale mock-up of the proposed cell. The easiest way to do this is to create a cardboard footprint, clearly marked with component in and out areas, control panels, safety switches, in effect all the features of the original that will be used.

Once these are constructed, and a cell put together, the operator will carry out a mock exercise using cycle and action times obtained from either the originals or manufacturers specifications.

As the name suggests, the Repetitive Task Observation Sheet is used to lay down on paper what the operators are doing from cycle to cycle. Before the team try and complete a Repetitive Task Observation Sheet, each member should be talked through the individual actions by the operator carrying out the tasks in order to gain a better understanding of the flow of the cell. It will make the completion an awful lot easier.

In addition to this, you may want to carry out a classroom exercise for a bit of practise. Using the Repetitive Action sheet, you can have the team time carrying out the following:

1. Rise out of your chair.
2. Walk to a flip chart.
3. Pick up a marker pen.
4. Remove the top.
5. Write your name on the chart.
6. Place the top back on the pen.
7. Replace the pen.
8. Return to the chair.
9. Sit down.

During this, you should add a few abnormal events, such as returning to the chair by a different route, writing your boss's name, dropping the pen and so on.

The Repetitive Task Observation Sheet is completed in the following manner.

Initially, write down the sequence of the operations that will be followed. This will save a mad rush when you are timing. Beware though, that what the operator says they will do and what they will actually do may differ.

What you will also have to consider in this is the time required to walk around the cell, if you think that it is significant. For instance, if the operator had to walk five metres between operations one and two, then the second operation quite clearly would not take twenty seconds. It would be twenty seconds minus the walking time.

1. As soon as the Operator has started the operations and has completed a few cycles, the Timer starts the stop-watch.
2. On the Repetitive Task Observation Sheet, the Timer will note the action being performed by the Operator, and the time that the action is completed is entered in the upper section of the column numbered 1, in the relevant row. The stop watch is not switched off but kept running. (Very similar to the Single Task Observation Sheet in the SMED section.)
3. Once the second action is completed the running time is again noted in the upper section of the column numbered 1, once more, in the relevant row.
4. The Timer carries on in this manner, noting all the times when each action is completed. Each time is noted down in the upper section of the corresponding action row and cycle column.
5. Once a complete cycle has been performed, the Operator will automatically return to action number 1. At this point the Timer carries on timing, placing the new times in column 2.
6. We carry on in this manner for ten complete cycles. The ten cycles allow us to obtain a decent amount of information whilst providing a safety net in the event of 'lost' times.

It is vitally important that all actions relating to any given operation are recorded. If the operator does something that was not written down on the sheet initially, then add it as a note. There will undoubtedly be one or two extra actions that the Operator will carry out. Keep a track of these in the Observations column along with the cycle number.

All actions must be noted.

Once the ten cycles have been timed, we will have to calculate the times required for each operation. This is fairly simple. What we have done is time the end of the operation, for instance 0:05 (zero minutes and 5 seconds). If the next operation has a finish time of 0:25 (zero minutes and 25 seconds), then we can say that the second operation took 20 seconds, in effect the time between the first operation finishing and the second operation finishing. Clear? This time should be added to the bottom section of each of the boxes, in a different colour to the original to provide a bit of clarity.

In the average time column, 'Av. Time', simply take an average of the individual times for that action. This is to include times that were abnormal, such as the 15 seconds taken up when the holder slipped, in our example below.

The 'Individual Cycle Time' row is the actual time taken for each cycle.

Where these two meet, the box has been split. This is to allow the sum of the average times and the average of the individual cycle times to be entered. These should be the same. However, if there are variances in rounding up the seconds in the averages, there will be a difference, admittedly of only a second or so, but the split box will allow both to be shown.

We will eventually end up with something like the following:

Sheet type - Kaizen, Single Task, Repetitive Task, Combination Sheet, Location, Problem Listing and Pareto, Time Observation

Location: Saw and lathe cell   Observer: WSR   Process: Saw and lathe
Date: 3/11/200-   Observation: Number 1   Component: M24x150 bolt
Time: 15.15

Action no	Descriptions and observations			Av time	1	2	3	4	5	6	7	8	9	10	11	12
1	Place unit in saw			5.0	0.05 --- 0/05	1.01 --- 0/06	1.55 --- 0.05	2.46 --- 0.06	3.39 --- 0.04	4.33 --- 0.06	5.27 --- 0.06	6.31 --- 0.05	7.22 --- 0.04	8.17 --- 0.06	---	---
2	Cut to size			19.0	0.25 --- 0.20	1.22 --- 0.20	2.13 --- 0.18	3.06 --- 0.20	3.58 --- 0.19	4.50 --- 0.17	5.45 --- 0.18	6.48 --- 0.17	7.40 --- 0.18	8.37 --- 0.20	---	---
3	Remove unit from saw and place in autolathe			6.0	0.30 --- 0.05	1.29 --- 0.07	2.19 --- 0.06	3.11 --- 0.05	4.03 --- 0.05	4.56 --- 0.06	5.52 --- 0.07	6.54 --- 0.06	7.47 --- 0.07	8.43 --- 0.06	---	---
4	Machine unit			15.0	0.47 --- 0.17	1.42 --- 0.13	2.33 --- 0.14	3.26 --- 0.15	4.18 --- 0.15	5.12 --- 0.16	6.06 --- 0.14	7.10 --- 0.16	8.02 --- 0.15	8.59 --- 0.16	---	---
5	Remove unit from lathe and place unit in holder. Holder slipped no 7			6.0	0.52 --- 0.05	1.46 --- 0.04	2.37 --- 0.04	3.31 --- 0.05	4.23 --- 0.05	5.17 --- 0.05	6.21 --- 0.15	7.14 --- 0.04	8.06 --- 0.04	9.04 --- 0.05	---	---
6	Pick up new unit and return to saw			4.0	0.55 --- 0.03	1.50 --- 0.04	2.40 --- 0.03	3.35 --- 0.04	4.27 --- 0.04	5.21 --- 0.04	6.26 --- 0.05	7.18 --- 0.04	8.11 --- 0.05	9.08 --- 0.04	---	---
				0.55 0.55	0.55	0.55	0.50	0.55	0.52	0.54	1.05	0.52	0.53	0.57		
					Individual cycle times											

This allows the team to determine the amount of time required to complete one cycle, in this case 55 seconds, with each action clearly distinguished.

The average times have been rounded up or down as you can't really time human actions to 10th's of a second. It's not the Olympics. Hence the need for the two times in the same box.

We can now plot this information on the Combination Sheet.

This is designed to show graphically the individual operations carried out within the cycle. As with some of the sheets that we have worked with in other sections, the information here is already available, but when seen in a graphic form it becomes more easily understood as well as letting other operators not participating see that something is actually being done and generating a bit of interest.

We split the actions up into three categories, Manual, Automatic and Walking, placing the relevant times into each box. It is possible to have Manual and Automatic times in the same row, with the different line styles telling the observer where the split in the times are. (For greater clarity you may want to use different colours, but remember this when printing off on a black ink printer if they are computer generated.) For instance, if the action was to be 'Place unit in CNC and machine' you would have a manual time for the un-loading and loading, with an automatic time for the actual machining.

Walking times tend to be on their own, as you generally do not carry out any operations whilst on the move. In the first instance shown the walking time line is actually run back to the start of the first action whilst maintaining its 4 second plot. This is purely due to the fact that it was the last action to be plotted.

The increments for the graphical representation of the times are once again dependant on the overall time and the space available.

The information obtained here in our example allows us to see that there is a lot of time spent waiting for automatic cycles to finish. From this we can ask questions and make recommendations. For instance, 'Why wait?'

We can also see that there is some time spent walking. This will allow the team to consider the positioning of machinery. Why walk so far?

There is also a Location Sheet shown, giving a brief outline of the cell. This is the same sheet that you would have seen in the SMED section and others, with slight style modifications to suit. One of these modifications can be the highlighting of areas that may be of interest or concern, for instance Quality, WIP and Safety issues (guards, interlocks etc.) being marked down. If WIP is present then take a note of the quantities.

And remember, this outline should be to scale if possible, as it will help in comparisons with others later on.

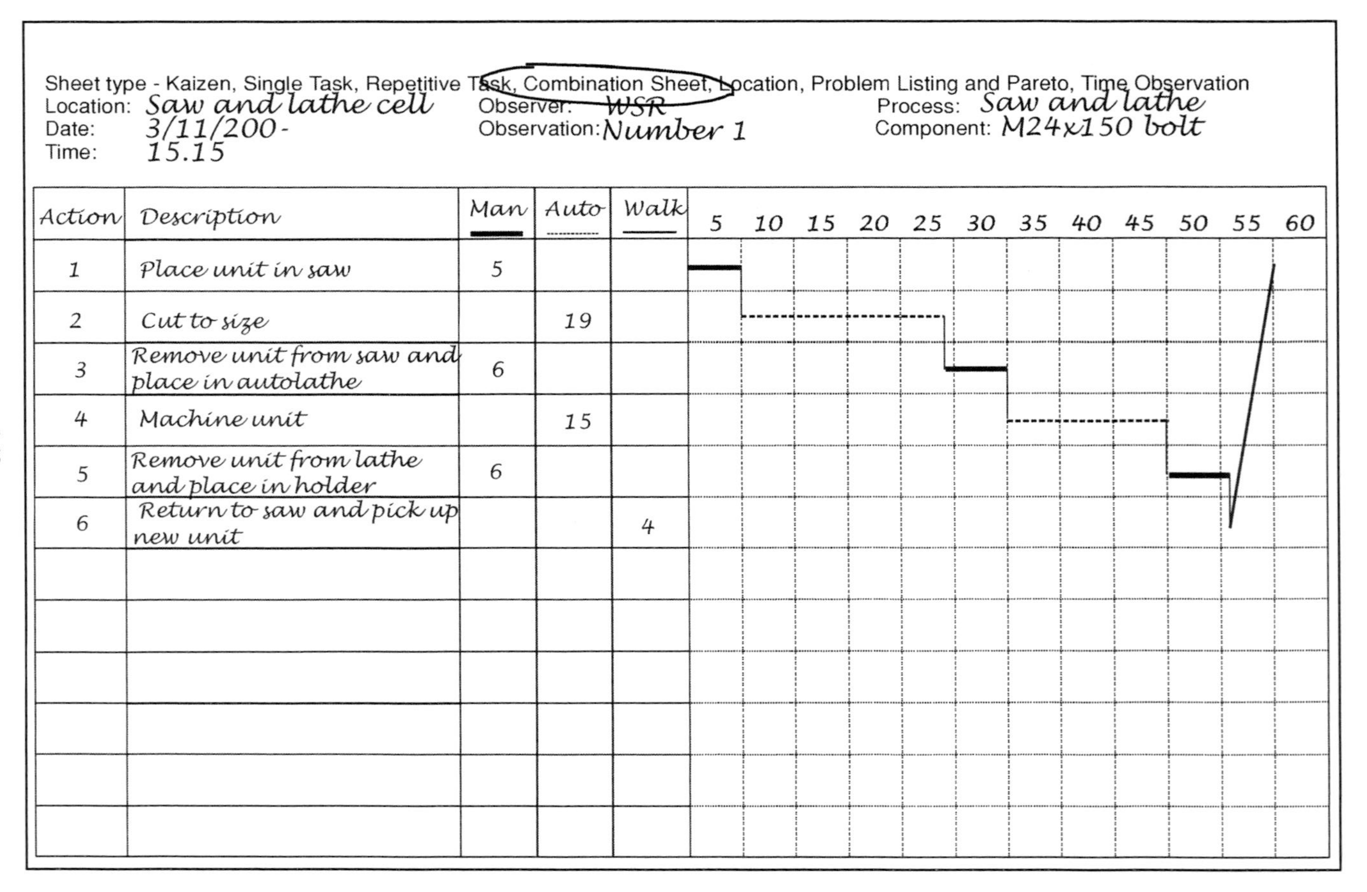

Sheet type - Kaizen, Single Task, Repetitive Task, Combination Sheet, Location, Problem Listing and Pareto, Time Observation

Location: Saw and lathe cell
Observer: WSR
Process: Saw and lathe

Date: 3/11/200-
Observation: Number 1
Component: M24x150 bolt

Time: 15.15

Action	Description	Man	Auto	Walk	5	10	15	20	25	30	35	40	45	50	55	60
1	Place unit in saw	5														
2	Cut to size		19													
3	Remove unit from saw and place in autolathe	6														
4	Machine unit		15													
5	Remove unit from lathe and place in holder	6														
6	Return to saw and pick up new unit			4												

Sheet type - Kaizen, Single Task, Repetitive Task, Combination Sheet, Location, Problem Listing and Pareto, Time Observation

Location: Saw and lathe cell   Observer: WSR   Process: Saw and lathe
Date: 3/11/200-   Observation: Number 1   Component: M24x150 bolt
Time: 15.15

Numbered	Description	Run	Elem	Int Ext	10 20 30 40 50 60 70 80 90 100 110 120
1	Place unit in saw				
2	Cut to size				
3	Remove unit from saw and place in autolathe				
4	Machine unit				
5	Remove unit from lathe and place in holder				
6	Return to saw and pick up new unit				

Lathe - 3
Saw - 1
Raw stock - 6
Holder - 5

Implement Ideas

With these three sheets there is enough information to start looking critically at the work area.

The Combination Sheet shows us that there is a lot of time spent waiting for machine cycles to finish so we must ask ourselves – what can we do with this time?

This same sheet shows us there are a number of seconds spent walking during each cycle. You may say that it is only 4 seconds per cycle but this equates to nearly 33 minutes in an eight hour day, for the given example. If the walk distance is only 5 metres, this works out as 2.5 km per day.

Take note: Every little bit helps.

As previously mentioned, it may be advantageous to carry out some timings and layouts with the use of paper cut-outs.

It may look silly at the time, but it is a lot easier to move a roll of paper then it is to move 4 machines.

Look at a different approach to the actions. What if we loaded the saw and the lathe and went on to do something else while waiting for them? Can we change the sequence of events to incorporate the automatic times?

If possible, move the machinery closer together. It saves a lot of shoe leather.

Try a range of ideas. Even if they seem idiotic, try them and see what happens. It is often the stupid ideas that bear the most fruit. (Generally because everyone else has said 'that'll never work' and so they were never tried out.)

- Be innovative.
- Don't be afraid of failure.
- Try the unexpected.

We must discuss the new sequence and take a note of it on the Repetitive Task Observation Sheet. *The team now follows what is written on the Sheet*, not the other way around.

As can be seen from the example, there is a huge reduction in cycle time, from 55 seconds down to 24 seconds.

The team must then complete the Combination Sheet and the Work Standardisation Sheet.

Let's see what happens:

Sheet type - Kaizen, Single Task, Repetitive Task, Combination Sheet, Location, Problem Listing and Pareto, Time Observation

Location: Saw and lathe cell | Observer: WSR | Process: Saw and lathe

Date: 3/11/200- | Observation: Number 2 | Component: M24x150 bolt

Time: 16.30

Action no	Descriptions and observations			Av time	1	2	3	4	5	6	7	8	9	10	11	12
1	Remove unit from saw place new unit. Start			13	0.06 --- 0.06	0.30 --- 0.13	0.54 --- 0.12	1.17 --- 0.13	1.41 --- 0.13	2.04 --- 0.12	2.29 --- 0.13	2.53 --- 0.13	3.15 --- 0.12	3.39 --- 0.13	---	---
2	Remove unit from lathe place new unit. Start			6	0.12 --- 0.06	0.36 --- 0.06	0.59 --- 0.05	1.23 --- 0.06	1.46 --- 0.05	2.10 --- 0.06	2.34 --- 0.05	2.58 --- 0.05	3.21 --- 0.06	3.44 --- 0.05	---	---
3	Place unit in holder			3	0.15 --- 0.03	0.40 --- 0.04	1.03 --- 0.04	1.26 --- 0.03	1.50 --- 0.04	2.13 --- 0.03	2.38 --- 0.04	3.01 --- 0.03	3.24 --- 0.03	3.47 --- 0.03	---	---
4	Return to saw and pick up new unit			2	0.17 --- 0.02	0.42 --- 0.02	1.04 --- 0.01	1.28 --- 0.02	1.52 --- 0.02	2.16 --- 0.03	2.40 --- 0.02	3.03 --- 0.02	3.26 --- 0.02	3.50 --- 0.03	---	---
				0.24 0.24	0.17	0.25	0.22	0.24	0.24	0.24	0.24	0.23	0.23	0.24		
						Individual cycle times										

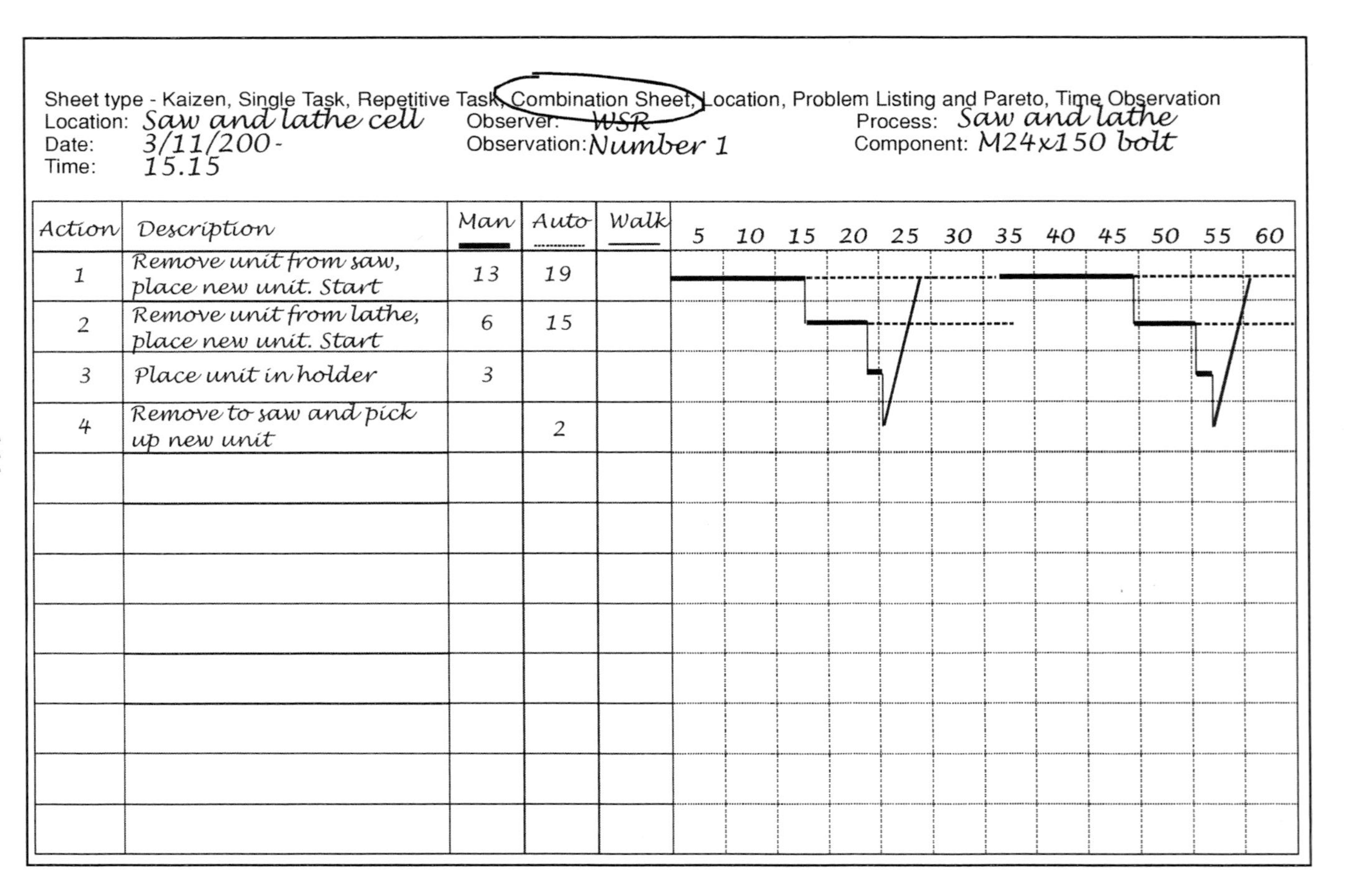

Sheet type - Kaizen, Single Task, Repetitive Task, Combination Sheet, Location, Problem Listing and Pareto, Time Observation

Location: Saw and lathe cell
Date: 3/11/200-
Time: 15.15
Observer: WSR
Observation: Number 1
Process: Saw and lathe
Component: M24x150 bolt

Action	Description	Man	Auto	Walk	5	10	15	20	25	30	35	40	45	50	55	60
1	Remove unit from saw, place new unit. Start	13	19													
2	Remove unit from lathe, place new unit. Start	6	15													
3	Place unit in holder	3														
4	Remove to saw and pick up new unit		2													

Sheet type - Kaizen, Single Task, Repetitive Task, Combination Sheet, Location, Problem Listing and Pareto, Time Observation

Location: Saw and lathe cell Observer: WSR Process: Saw and lathe
Date: 3/11/200- Observation: Number 1 Component: M24x150 bolt
Time: 15.15

Numb-ered	Description	Run	Elem	Int Ext	10	20	30	40	50	60	70	80	90	100	110	120
1	Place unit in saw															
2	Cut to size															
3	Remove unit from saw and place in autolathe															
4	Machine unit															
5	Remove unit from lathe and place in holder															
6	Return to saw and pick up new unit															

Lathe - 2
Saw - 1
Raw stock - 4
Holder - 3

The exciting Takt time bit

The Combination Sheet clearly shows that in this example the operator is still waiting for the saw to finish its cycle. (Eight seconds wait in fact). This additional free time can be put to good use with the introduction of extra work such as the final action of the last operation or the first action of the following operation, thereby freeing up other operators.

This highlights an important aspect of Work Standardisation, namely **Operator Loading**. Operator Loading is the matching up of manning levels with Work Standardisation with takt time. A diagram will be very helpful here, and this is also where we bring back the Takt time analysis.

For the example we will assume that we have been following cell 4. We will also assume that the takt time is greater than the cycle time, and will put a figure of 65 seconds on the takt time.

If the process that we were following was only one of a number of processes in the manufacturing of the component, what might our operator loading look like after the exercise? As you can see, Cell one is running at approximately 40% of Takt time, 2 is over 65%, 3 is at about 60% and 4 is having an easy time of it at about 30%.

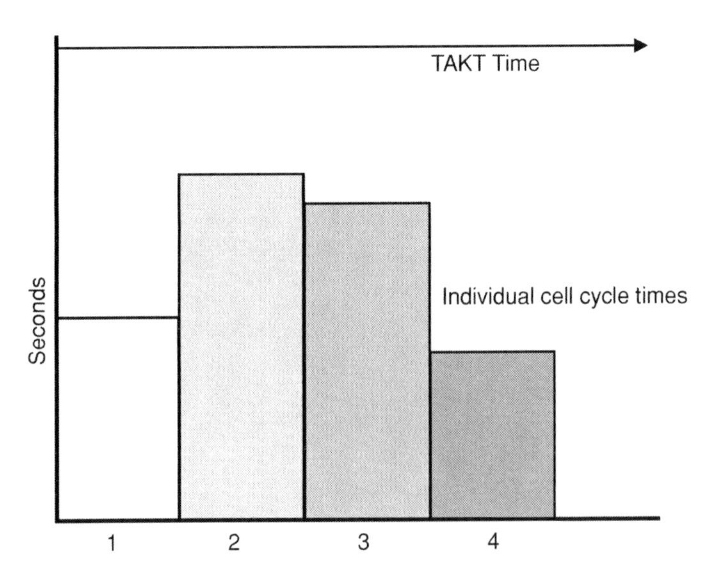

The four operators are all performing within the takt time, at an average of 49%. There is no point in them running 100% of the time because after 49%

of the shift they will be manufacturing goods that are not required. Likewise, if they carry on in this manner until they reach the daily requirements, the remaining 51% of the time they will not be doing anything, but will still have to be paid. However, with Work Standardisation we can balance the line better and load the operators more efficiently:

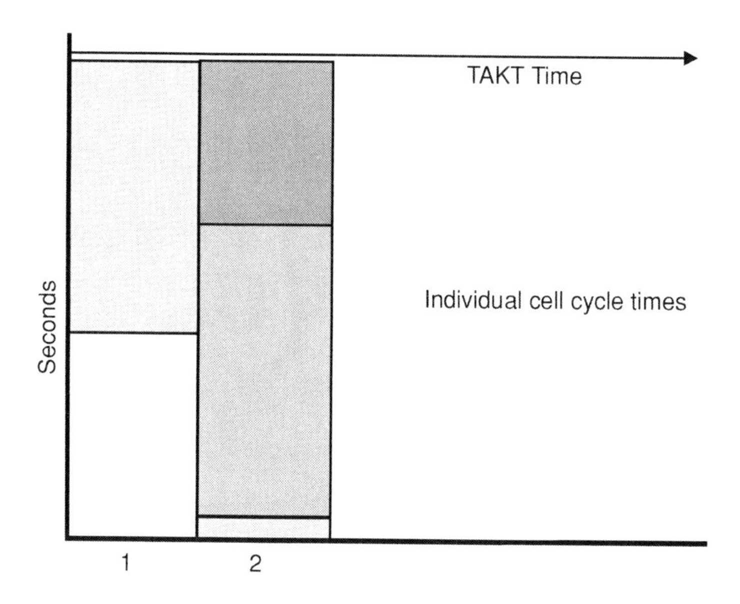

As you can see, we have moved nearly all of the actions from operator 2 onto operator 1, and placed all of the work from operators 3 and 4 onto 2, simply by loading them up to the takt time.

The analysis work that you completed, through the use of the Repetitive Task Observation Sheet et al, will detail what percentage of the takt time the operators are working to. From here, it is possible to calculate the total number of operators required in the overall process.

The mathematics is simple. Using a Takt time of 65 seconds, the cycle time for the four cells totals 127 seconds, therefore 1.95 people can operate this line at a cycle time of 63 seconds each.

Using percentages you will note that the above total 195%, therefore two people can run the cells at less than 100%.

If all of the operations require, say, 100 seconds to complete, and the takt time is ten seconds, then in theory you require 10 operators loaded to ten seconds each.

Likewise, if the cycle time total is 50 seconds and the takt time 100 seconds, then you require 0.5 people, or one person for half of the production time.

Now this is very handy when just making figures up, therefore in the real world you may have to have one operator loaded to 85% and another loaded to 99% in order to achieve this.

This is easy to do with cellular manufacturing, as you can create one large cell comprising all machinery instead of 4-off smaller cells, and balance the workload.

It is therefore vitally important that, when carrying out Work Standardisation, you split the actions down to their simplest level, where each second is accounted for, in order to achieve best balance, as will be seen from the following. The example is simple, but in practise it is generally feasible simply to move actions and operations down the line. You may have to chop and change – for instance if using more than two operators then operator 1 may have to do some of operator 3's work, as the diagrams will show:

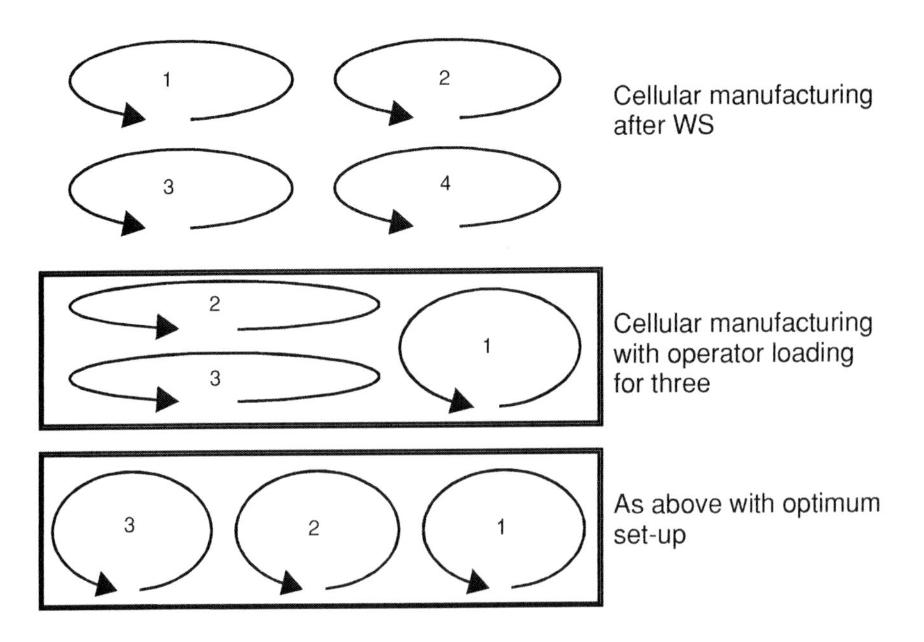

You can clearly see the advantages of the Operator Loaded manner of approach, but you can also see from this that in the second scenario operators 2 and 3 have to walk back to the start point after each of their cycles. Operator 1 naturally returns to the start, so there is no time lost in walking, and no sore feet at the end of the shift also.

With the third scenario, all operators return to the start as part of the overall cycle, but the numbering of their actions might be operator 1 carried out operations 1 through to 5 and 25 to 30, number 2 carries out 6 to 10 and 20 to 24 and operator number 3 carries out 11 to 19. Make sense?

The approach used here is of particular benefit when your supply requirements vary from day to day or hour to hour. The cycle times remain the same but the Takt times vary, therefore having your cells set up correctly and all of the information in front of you lets you see at a glance who goes where to complete what number of operations at the maximum possible loading. Beware though, that if machine cycle times become longer than the varying Takt times then it is not simply a case of altering the amount of operators, you will have to work extra hours. This should be evident from the Combination Sheet.

If you find yourself in this type of scenario, then it is beneficial to have pre-planned setups for ranges of Takt times, clearly laid out so the operators know what is required of them. For instance if the Takt time is above 30 seconds then only one operator is required, if it is between 20 and 30 seconds then two operators are needed and if it is below 20 then three are required.

You may want to colour code your cell machinery – green marked machines are for single operator use, blue and red marked machines are for two operator use and yellow, white and black marked machines are for three operator use.

You do not have to run the cells fully manned either. If two operators are required, then you could realistically have a percentage split in the work load. Say actions one and two take 12 seconds each, therefore every 12 seconds there is a component requiring action three. If action three takes 6 seconds to complete then you only need to work for half the amount of time.

Following this, operator one completes actions one and two, producing 300 components in one hour. Every half hour operator two commences action 3, taking half an hour in total to complete what was already made by operator one as well as what operator one makes whilst operator 2 is working away at the backlog. This then allows operator 2 to carry out additional work somewhere else.

Back to the Paperwork

The Combination Sheet shows the sequence of actions that form the process, and **this will be used as the standard procedure**, the Work Standardisation.

The Location Sheet also shows that the walking distance is greatly reduced.

All of the above, operator loading and split processing, are relevant whether there are any great savings to be made or not as you should be looking to load your workforce and workplace to the maximum.

Re-using the 'Problem Listing and Pareto'

The Problem Listing and Pareto is very useful in this instance, subject to a few small changes, in that it documents downtime and operators actions that may not at first be apparent, such as tool changes (drill bits etc), maintenance, oiling, a whole host of items. It should be used as a part of the operator's ongoing paperwork and should be maintained in the work area for the required amount of time. However, we do not want to bog the operators down with paperwork, therefore it should be a temporary initiative. This means that you have to act on the information gathered on these sheets, once more looking to increase the CPE. The next time that you carry out a review of the area, introduce a new sheet for a fresh perspective.

In addition to highlighting extra activities that the operators have to carry out, these sheets can also be used to record specific downtime reasons – every time the machines switch off, the operator records what the problem is and the time taken to correct it. In this instance it may be better to enter seconds or minutes as these niggly little problems usually only require a quick fix. This additional information can be used to pinpoint areas where simple steps can be taken to increase your performance.

Refer once again to the SMED section for additional help on actions such as tool changes, changeovers and any other relevant actions that cause downtime. The additional downtime issues noted here can help to form the basis of TPM, referencing items such as oil levels, pressures, safety switches, guards, operating temperatures etc.

The information gained here can be used to re-evaluate the actual work-load of the operators for items such as Takt Time and Cycle Time comparisons, as well as providing a more accurate account of downtime, allowing us to re-evaluate production targets.

Sheet type - Kaizen, Single Task, Repetitive Task, Combination Sheet, Location, Problem Listing and Pareto, Time Observation

Location: *Saw and lathe cell* Observer: *WSR* Process: *Saw and lather*

Date: *3/11/200-* Observation: *Sheet 1* Component: *M24 x 150 Bolt*

Time: *Day shift*

Numbered	Concerns, measured as individuals				Stoppage 1st	2nd	3rd	4th	5th	Minutes 2	4	6	8	10	12	Tot
1	Oil machine				1.30	2.00	1.00	2.30								7.00
2	Replace drill bit				4.45	5.00	3.50									13.35
3	Adjust clamping				1.00											1.00
4	Adjust feed plates				0.45	1.15										2.00
5	Collect raw stock				7.00											7.00
																30.35

The sheets should also be numbered in the event that more than one is required.

Finally

You are now in possession of a large amount of paperwork, some of which we know is just a part of the ongoing exercise. However, the Combination Sheets that we have re-written to use as Work Standardisation should be followed rigorously and used in training and ongoing operator evaluations. They must be placed where operators can easily access them, not just the personnel who are associated with that particular area, but available to anyone who wishes to see examples of Lean Production in operation. All the information concerning the Work Standardisation can be obtained by referencing these sheets.

There should be no excuses for not following this sequence.

It should be adhered to at all times.

The monitor for the system put in place will be the continued production at the required output within the given time.

Basically, if the system is failing, then you will have less components and your CPE figure will drop.

Kanban – Stock Re-ordering Systems

The word 'kanban' is Japanese for 'advertising hoarding'. A kanban card, described later, is merely an advert giving the message 'Produce components for me.'

As mentioned in the introduction on why we should be looking at Lean Production systems, the 7 Wastes of manufacturing were listed. Three of these can be addressed through the introduction of a Kanban system – Poor Quality, Panic Production and Stock levels.

The premise of the system is simple – your supplier will not manufacture components unless they are wanted by yourself. This is a 'pull' system, where goods are pulled from further upstream as required, as opposed to a 'push' system where you make goods and send them to the next stage, whether required or not.

Therefore this leads to less inventory, less risk of large scale quality defects and eliminates panic production. (Likewise, you should not be looking to produce unless your customers require the stock.)

However, as with most things, there is a slight variation. Your supplier may hold a small amount of stock in order to supply you immediately but as soon as that stock is starting to move then they will trigger production.

Remember – your supplier is the person one up the line, not necessarily a separate company, just as your customer is the person one down the line, not the end user.

One drawback with a kanban system – there needs to be stock in the system for it to work. And stock in the system is money tied up that could be released for other projects/investments. Therefore, we will look at a few manufacturing situations, each one getting better than the last. However, the one we will be considering is a middle-of-the-road compromise between very poor production techniques and a state of the art system that is very difficult to achieve.

We will consider two types of systems:

1. those that use cards as the trigger
2. those that use a visual form as the trigger.

A brief overview

Imagine a manufacturing plant with a large number of separate production areas. It is not always possible to create a one-piece flow system, for whatever reasons, and you may have a large capital casting machine supplying four separate machining cells. As with most manufacturing plants, you will hopefully have at least one day's notice of what your requirements are.

We will use the following information. The following shows manufacturing and production capacities:

1. Manufacturing cell number	1	2	3	4
2. Number of component types	3	4	3	2
3. Capacity per 8-hour day	1.5K	2K	1K	1.5K
4. Requirements for a 5-day week per component [(Item 3 *5)/Item2]	2.5K	2.5K	1.6K	3.75K

These cells are supplied by a casting machine. This is capable of producing 4,000 components per 8 hour shift. The above requirements tell us that we will have to cast for 12 hours per day. This is the total capacity for all 4 cells, 6,000, divided by the casting capacity of 4,000 per 8 hours, giving 12 hours run time.

There are a number of ways that stock can be held.

Traditional method

There are a number of areas within the manufacturing site that hold stock and each of these areas allows for a huge margin of safety. For instance, if the end customer required 2.5K of each component per week, then each area will hold 2.5K of that component at all times as a minimum.

When the end customer wants, the end customer gets. When an order comes through, Dispatch will move to the production area and after spending a large amount of time actually trying to locate components, they will take as many parts as they can find or until the area set aside for these parts in Dispatch is full. All this dependant of course on the parts being available.

The whole process is controlled by people with lots of experience at fire fighting, running around in a panic trying to ensure that they can meet the customers requirements. If a production run is required in a hurry, another job will be knocked back in order to ensure that the panic order is completed, and so on. This decreases efficiency as more unplanned changeovers are brought into the production day.

The whole of the manufacturing plant is full of inventory, there is no control over stock re-ordering or manufacturing, WIP is all over the plant, customer supply is injured, quality suffers and nobody sleeps at night. The amount of WIP may be in the hundreds of thousands when on a weekly basis you are having to deliver 30,000.

The plant looks like the following:

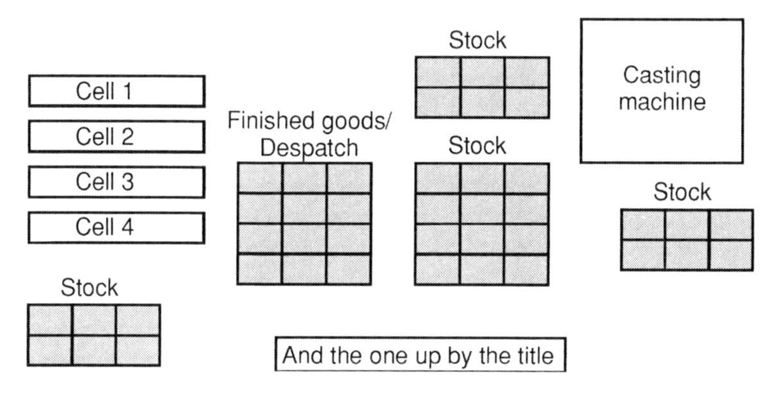

Getting there

If the demand is fairly constant, it can be averaged out over a long time span, or at least regularly modified, and the company can take the decision to follow a set production plan. This entails producing enough of each component to allow every other component to be manufactured before the stock of the first component runs out. For instance, for one weeks rolling manufacturing plan, with components being removed on a daily basis, the weekly demands are as follows:

Cell	1			2				3			4	
Components	3			4				3			2	
Order	1	2	3	4	5	6	7	8	9	10	11	12
Amount (000s)	2.5	2.5	2.5	2.5	2.5	2.5	2.5	1.6	1.6	1.6	3.75	3.75

The company and operators know from one day to the next what is required. SMED preparation teams are aware of what is required.

However, there are nearly 60,000 components being held in stock at any one time. WIP is held between casting and machining, and after machining as finished goods.

What happens is the customer suddenly asks for an additional order?

What happens if they suddenly do not need to collect a component one day?

The whole system goes down the pan. You end up producing more than is required or you short the customer.

There are many opportunities for large scale quality problems.

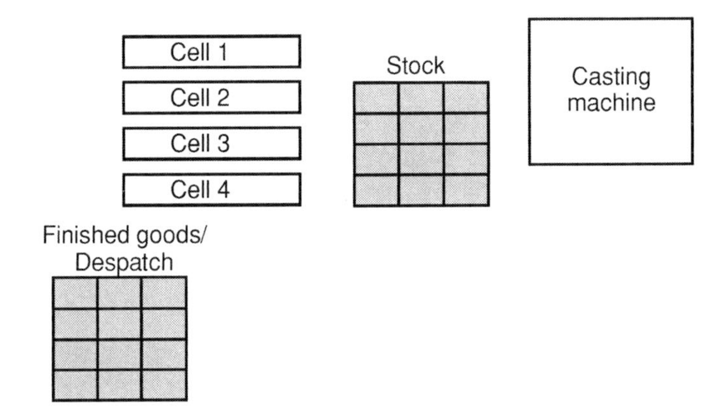

Getting better

The weekly requirements are the same, so the last table above is still relevant as far as amounts are concerned.

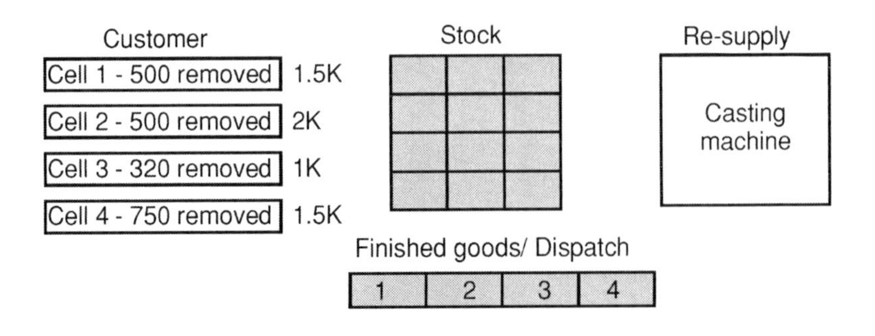

The amounts shown being removed (1.5K, 2K, 1K, 1.5K) are the daily requirements from each individual cell.

What you remove from the WIP between casting and machining is exactly what the customer requires for delivery. Very rarely does a company have to supply immediately, (exceptions in the main are the chilled food sector, where the company may have only three or four hours in which to complete an order), so what you are doing here is manufacturing on Monday what your customer requires on Tuesday. You are removing from Stock the customer requirements, triggering the casting to start once again. Therefore, what appears in your Finished Goods/Dispatch area on Monday night are items that will be collected on Tuesday.

The amount of WIP is reduced from circa 60,000 to around the 34,000 mark. (30K between casting and machining, 4K in finished goods)

This situation allows stock to be held for removal and replaced on a daily level. The company may not know exactly from one day to the next what is required, but once again the stock levels between casting and machining can be averaged out from either historical records or future order contracts.

One very important point to notice however – you are moving from 2.5 casting changeovers per day on average to 12. SMED work is required here.

(Read on – this is the scenario that is best suited to the kanban system. We will look at the next steps from here, but the scene shown above is the one most relevant to the majority of business.)

Better still

Ideally, you do not want to start producing components until your customer requires them. We have already looked at the reasons behind this, but primarily if you work on a component, you are adding value to it and this is a cost without any revenue coming in to pay for this work.

Therefore don't do anything until the market asks for it. How do we do this? Take a look at the following:

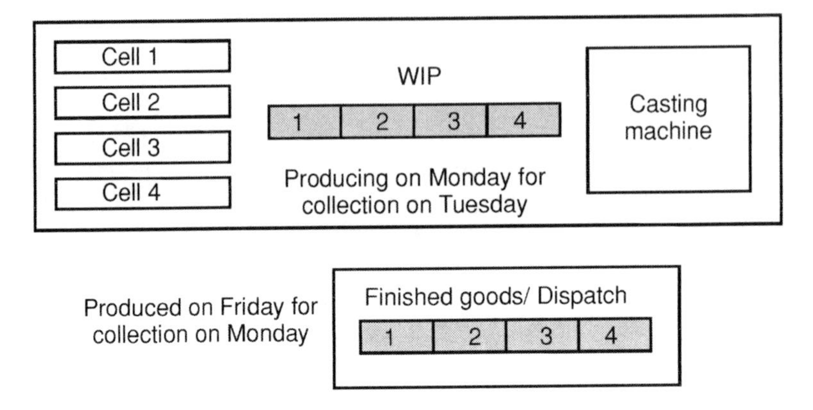

The production team will in the main have at least one working day's warning as far as requirements are concerned, therefore the casting machine starts casting the day prior to collection, these castings being passed down the line to the machining cells throughout the day.

WIP is reduced to the absolute minimum (see additional to this below), any quality issues can be addressed before the problem becomes critical, and production is controlled by the customer, not an office full of production schedulers.

The Best

This situation will be very difficult to achieve, nearly impossible (nearly), but with time, effort and a lot of hard work it can be reached. We stated above that you should not produce until the customer requires the component, so:

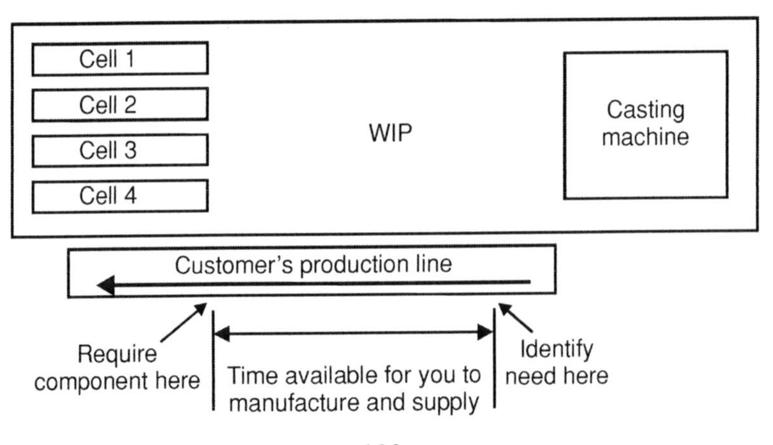

What has happened here is that your customer has recognised a need for a component, informed you of that need, you have manufactured the component, delivered it to the customer, the component has been fitted, and the need for the next component has been identified. You do not hold any stock and the only WIP is the specific item that the customer has requested.

For instance, you supply a car manufacturing plant with the products manufactured in the four cells above, 1-4. The car plant production line is capable of handling four types of car simultaneously, each one of which requires products from either cell 1, 2, 3 or 4. As the car enters the work area information is sent to you, as supplier, saying for instance 'supply me with component A from cell 3'. What you would then do is changeover, if required, the casting machine to produce one off of component number 3, transfer it to cell 3, alter it to type A and deliver to the car plant work area where it is required – all within the time taken for the car to enter the work area and reach the specific point where the production line worker commences fitting item A to the car. That is the best scenario. Read this though:

Minimum WIP – the absolute minimum for WIP is 1 (if you have a WIP of 0, you have no work). This is the classic 'by the book' figure put on it, and this is correct, but as stated in other sections, we are working in the real world. With WIP of 1, the customer requires one component, triggering your company to make only that one component as required.

In a lot of cases in Japan, companies collect from each other every 15 minutes, calculated to include factors such as traffic jams, mechanical breakdown of vans, cyclists and a whole host of other items/problems.

You already know that your customer collects dozens or hundreds at a time, on a daily basis, so don't worry in the short term about reaching WIP=1.

Back to our little example – As it takes 12 hours to cast 8 hours worth of machining WIP, how do you keep your cells busy?

There are two ways in which to do this:

1. Production times are 12 hours for casting and 8 hours for machining. Simply start casting 4 hours before the machining cells come on-line.
2. After Work Standardisation, Takt time analysis, cell construction and a greater understanding of Lean Production, you will be able to either make up this 33% deficit or balance the cells to work over the 12 hours.

Beware though, that if you follow the latter route you may have to double shift.

How are we going to implement this Kanban?

System 1 – Cards

Kanban cards are introduced to the system to trigger production. In the 'Better Still' scenario above, we are producing only what the customer requires, but we do have a day's notice of that requirement, therefore we can not say that this is a true kanban system. We have to take a step further back, to the 'Getting Better' section, before we can achieve a clearer picture of how kanban will operate.

The customer demand is taken by the machining cells from the Stock area between the cells and the casting machine. (Bear in mind that this area holds one week's stock.) Daily demands are 500, 500, 320 and 750 for each type of component. If for cell one there are 50 components in a box, then you may have to remove 10 boxes per component (50 x10 = 500).

Within each box there will be a kanban card. As this box is removed from the Stock area, the card travels with it to the machining area. Only once the box has been completely emptied of components is the card removed from the box and placed in a 'post-box'. The fact that the card is now in the 'post-box' shows that:

'one box of component X has been removed from the Stock area, X has been machined completely and is ready to proceed to the next operation.'

The cards in the post-box are collected by the casting machine operator. The operator now has a list of all the stock that has been removed, therefore he is in a position to replenish that stock by setting the casting machine up to suit.

What do the cards look like?

There are a number of different card types – triangular, circular, rectangular, metal, paper etc, every type that you can think of. Do what best suits your needs. However, all of them contain a standard range of information:

- Part description
- Part number
- Quantity per container/card (This is the re-order quantity)
- Area where the card is used

They may look like the following:

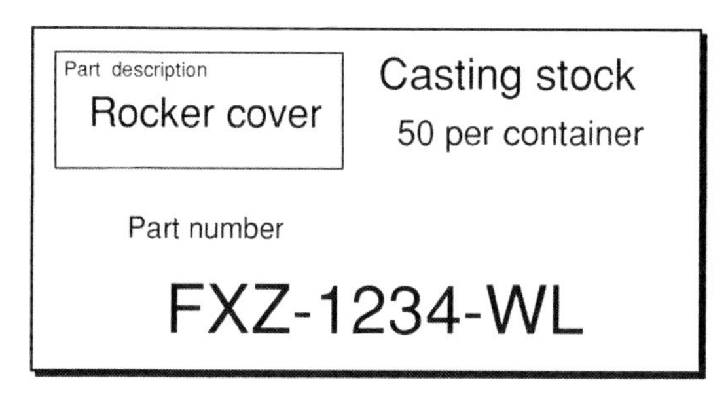

It is common for cards to be easily identifiable between operations, so for instance all cards from the casting/stock/machining area will be a specific colour irrespective of component that they identify. This allows you to know at what stage of the process a component is in.

These cards will be returned to the post-box when the components have been fully machined. At some specified point in the day, the machine operator will empty the post-box, gather up the cards and decide on the order of manufacture to replenish stock. He will look to replenish this stock in the pre-calculated amount of time, in this instance 12 hours casting to supply eight hours' worth of machining. These cards will then be placed in completed boxes of cast components and returned to the stock area. You will note that the casting operator only produces enough components to refill the specific amount noted on the cards. This reduces stock to the minimum amount calculated to keep the plant going.

If we look at one step further back again, we can see how, with more stock in the system, the entire production area can be considered. The following was based around the rolling production plan. However, if you do want to run with large stock quantities until you get your SMED or TPM projects completed, then this set-up will remove the need for the rolling plan and the associated problems. (This is complicated, so bear with me.)

Yellow cards – customer to finished goods, all components.

Blue cards – finished goods to machining cells, all components.

Purple cards – machining cells to stock to casting sections, all components.

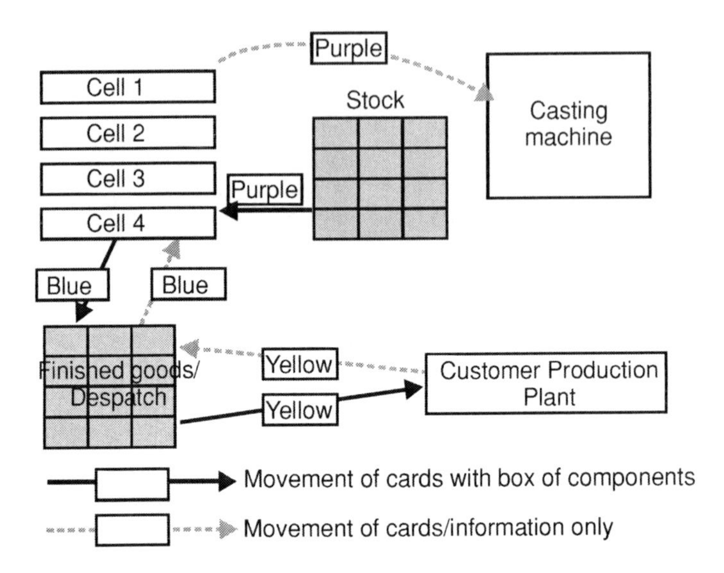

1. The customer will send in a transport lorry to collect their requirements. (We will say on a daily basis). This amount will be removed from dispatch depending on the number of yellow cards that the lorry driver has. The final customer has given the lorry driver ten Kanban cards and told them to 'collect these'. 10 cards = 10 boxes of components removed.
2. The blue cards are removed from the finished stock containers and replaced with the yellow cards. This shows that the containers are now in a state where they are about to be taken by the customer. The blue cards are taken to the machining cells in order to trigger production.
3. The machining cells operators check the part number on the blue cards and remove from the Stock area containers of the corresponding components. These containers have purple cards. The purple cards stay with the boxes until the last component has been removed, at which point the purple card is placed in the post-box, ready to be collected by the casting machine operator.
4. Once the last component in any box has undergone all operations, it is placed in the box that will carry it to the finished goods/dispatch area. (It must have had the corresponding blue card placed into it before any finished goods were placed there.) This shows that the box is full to the specified number and that all components have been machined. Once

returned to the finished goods/dispatch area it is ready for collection by the customer.

All boxes that are used for specific components must contain the same amount of components in the various areas, otherwise a card from one area will not correspond with amounts from another and confusion as to the amount of stock in the system will begin to creep in.

You will notice that any box, at any stage of the process, contains a card. This is to ensure that identification can be carried out at any point.

System 2: Visual

Instead of using cards to trigger production on an hourly/daily/weekly basis, a visual system can be employed. This uses the removal of containers to highlight a sign that triggers the next stage up-stream to start producing.

As an example, if you are filling a roller belt with boxes and relying on gravity to move the boxes down the track, at a pre-set point on the track there will be a sign that is basically informing you that:

'You have reached the minimum re-order level. Start producing now'

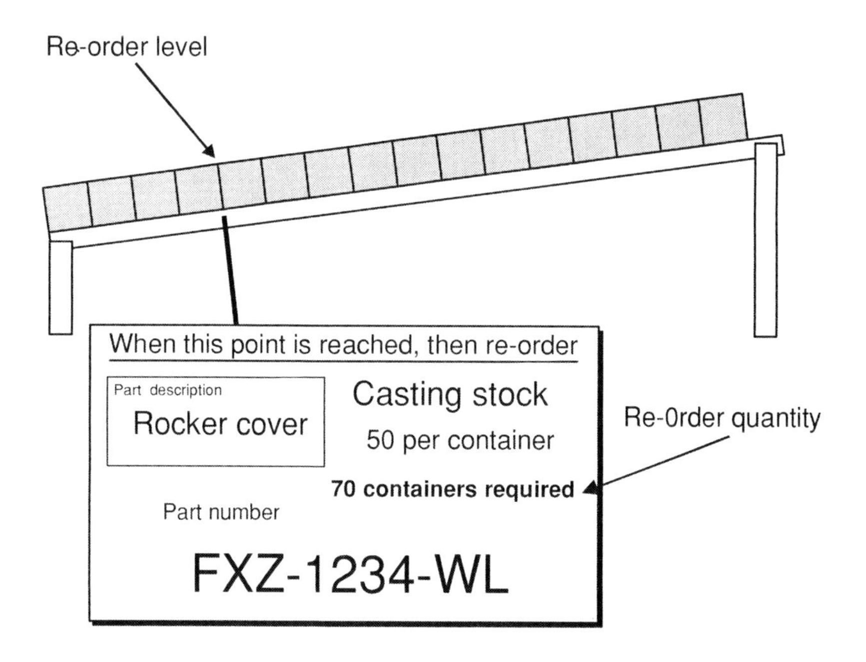

Re-order Level vs Re-order Quantity

There is a difference. The re-order level is the amount of stock that you have left when you ask for more. Re-order quantity is the amount that you ask for. And so production starts.

The secret here is to ensure that the lead time for replacement parts is less than the time the existing parts will last for. If your lead time is two days, and you use ten boxes per day, then your minimum re-order level will have to be at least twenty boxes. Anything less and you are going to run out.

In addition, if you need 50 boxes to fill the conveyor once again, do not re-order 50 if the lead time is two days. In those two days you will have used an additional 20 boxes, so re-order 70 boxes.

If your two areas are separated and a direct visual approach is not feasible, then simply have a pre-printed tick-sheet with all part numbers and descriptions on that is passed upstream on an hourly/daily/weekly basis. This acts as the trigger.

This is a very simple form of kanban and easy to implement. However, beware – with cards you are looking in the main to replace within a time period what was removed from stores within a similar time period. With the visual system you may find that more components run out than you are capable of replacing within the given time.

Perhaps you may have 20 separate components that are all just above the minimum re-order level. If all 20 are ordered at once, upstream production may struggle to cope.

'How can this be?' you may ask. The re-order levels may be more than just one day's production, say five days' worth. Multiply this by 20 and that is a lot of production. With cards, you are only looking to replace perhaps one day's worth.

As stated earlier, kanban is a simple premise but there is a lot of number crunching required in order to implement a good system in the first place.

And that will be site specific.

How do we calculate the amount of kanban cards/containers?

There is a simple equation here:

$$\text{Number of Kanban} = \frac{\text{Daily Usage} \times (\text{Leadtime} + \text{Safety margin} + \text{Amount of days' stock in system})}{\text{Container capacity}}$$

$$\frac{500 \times (1[day] + 0.5[days] + 0[days]}{50}$$
$$= 15 \text{ containers}$$

You now know that there are 15 containers required to provide your daily needs including safety stock of 0.5 days in case of drastic mechanical breakdown, lorry crashes, customer rush orders etc. (This safety factor is specific to your own production plant – it could be 0.5 days, it could be three weeks. Likewise, if using cards, then 'Amount of days Stock in the system' will equal zero and if using a visual system the amount will be determined by the figures that you feel comfortable with – whatever suits your needs depending on the overall systems in place. Do not be too clever or lean though – there are dozens of stories of companies using taxis, helicopters or private jets to move components between plants due to unforeseen circumstances. Remember, if you stop a car plant from manufacturing because you haven't delivered product X, they will reclaim the lost production costs from you.)

Even though you only require 10 boxes per day, try and keep all 15 boxes in the system and rotate the stock. Do not keep a separate 'safety stock area'. This ensures that you know at all times the true amount of stock in the system, and any quality problems can be traced immediately.

And that is basically it. A lot of description and waffle to put across a simple idea. Kanban is a good system, but to actually put the idea across and implement it in the production plant takes a lot of thought. Good luck.

If you follow these rules things should go according to plan:

1. Production downstream only removes from stock what is required.
2. Production upstream only replaces what was removed.
3. Quality must be spot on – 100% at all time, otherwise part boxes are generated.
4. Kanban cards should be used throughout the entire system for traceability.
5. The greater the amount of stock, the greater number of opportunities to reduce that stock. More stock = more production problems.

In keeping with item 5, and in an attempt to emulate those that have gone before, you will all have seen the following diagram:

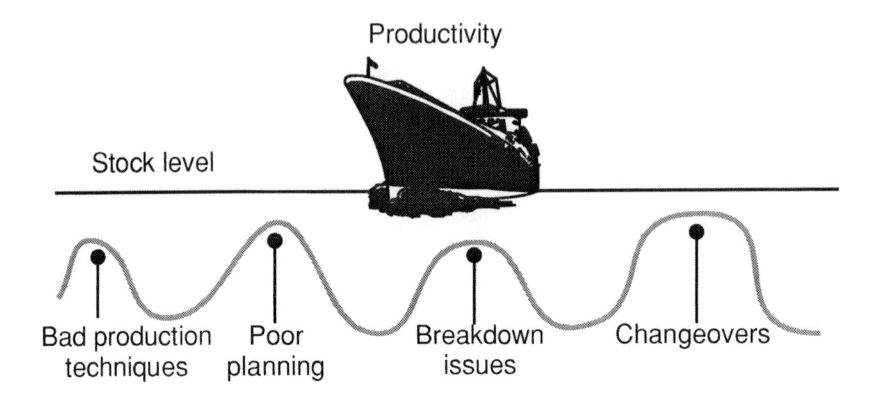

As the levels of stock are reduced, there is less of a comfort zone when things go wrong. So as the stock levels fall, problems such as those shown above will be highlighted, and the good ship Productivity will flounder. Use kanban to drive improvements.

Finally, so you are aware that such things do exist:

Jidoka Boxes

Some companies have Jidoka boxes fitted to their production sites. These are a set of boxes that split the working day up into hours, e.g. 8 boxes for an 8 hour day. The daily requirements are split up into complete amounts of containers, for instance 8 containers instead of 7.47 containers, each containing 20 components. This is designed to allow production to be smoothed throughout the day.

The customer will only order in multiples of twenty, to ensure that every container delivered to them is full. So, if a customer requires 80 components per day, this equals 4 boxes of 20 components, and the working day is split up into 4 sections. Easy, 8 hours split into 4 equals 2 hours; this means that once dispatch find out in the morning what the daily requirements are, they will place the equivalent amount of kanban cards into the Jidoka box, each against a set time, and a container will be collected by dispatch from production at those designated times, see below. This triggers production to start producing in order to replace the removed container. All very sensible.

It is not as simple as that though. The cards are placed in the boxes by a predetermined, and some would say random, order.

Order	**1**	**7**	**6**	**2**	**5**	**3**	**8**	**4**
Time	6	7	8	9	10	11	12	13
Cards	*			*		*		*

What happens if the customer requires 60 components? That is three boxes, three trips to production by dispatch personnel. The Jidoka box has three cards placed into it, against set times of 06:00, 09:00 and 11:00.

Order	**1**	**7**	**6**	**2**	**5**	**3**	**8**	**4**
Time	6	7	8	9	10	11	12	13
Cards	*			*		*		

Likewise for 100 components:

Order	**1**	**7**	**6**	**2**	**5**	**3**	**8**	**4**
Time	6	7	8	9	10	11	12	13
Cards	*			*	*	*		*

All very simple and neat. And extremely inefficient. Remember, the real world. This system is obviously capable of turning out 160 components/8 containers per shift, as there are 8 separate Jidoka boxes. So what do you do if only 80 components are required? Do you have people standing around waiting for dispatch personnel to turn up and trigger production once again? No.

Outwith the real world, this system is designed to allow all production to flow smoothly throughout the day, with personnel moving in and out of production areas as and when required.

Jidoka boxes are great in theory. We won't be looking too closely at them.

Planning a Kaizen Event

One of the main emphases of introducing Continuous Improvement is the active participation of the workforce. As I've mentioned many times, they make up the backbone of any project team and are the ones who should be providing, after a bit of persuasion, the main ideas towards making the specifics work. Before attempting to introduce a system though, they will need to be made aware of the entire Continuous Improvement philosophies and ideas, and this can be completed through the use of small lectures, worked examples and initial handouts.

There must be some method by which ideas can be brought to the fore, and this must be controlled otherwise you will have teams working only on projects and not on manufacturing. A simple suggestion scheme or sheet will suffice, with personnel giving brief notes on what they think can be achieved, the potential costs and payback or benefits. Review team recommendations should also be given on this sheet to act as feedback to the originator. This is shown under the 'Improvement Initiation Sheet'.

This sheet fits into the overall system as shown on the flow diagram. There must be a review team decision on all proposals, with either a rejection, kaizen or project being agreed upon. From here the review team can determine goals and objectives and allocate resources as required.

They should not act alone in this process, and the participation of shop floor supervisors, managers etc. should be actively sought. The initiators of the idea should also play an active role, whether they will be involved in the final event or not.

The following flow sheet also shows the Plan-Do-Check-Act cycle. The review team should hold responsibility for ensuring that all previous events and projects are still running at the correct levels of efficiency.

The Kaizen Preparation Check Sheet is invaluable in that it lets the entire workforce know what events are imminent. The check list can be altered to suit, however the plant must be capable of performing and the personnel in the team must be aware. Use of the sheet reduces last minute panic.

The Kaizen Monitor is purely a 'before and after' view of the project, and is helpful in presentations to management and shop floor on the success of the event.

Implementing Continuous Improvements

A quick page of advice and guidance regarding the teams, the events and the monitoring systems.

As we have gone along, I have mentioned the make-up of teams in only two areas, SMED and TPM, mainly due to the fact that these are generally large, intensive and time consuming projects that need a lot of skilled work completed in a short period of time. Regarding the other areas, these can be carried out by small groups, two or three people even, without any detrimental impact on their effectiveness. In some cases, smaller groups will be preferable.

If you have never carried out any CI initiatives in the past, then it will really be a case of suck it and see, at least until you get your footing.

The actual implementation of the events can vary massively. You may take an hour to look at a SMED issue on a small press, just three people say, or a fortnight to analyse a 2,000 tonne closing pressure, high temperature injection moulding plant. Obviously the larger the project then the more time consuming it will be, but the small press mentioned above?

Perhaps twenty minutes observing the workings and discussing as the machine is producing. A further ten minutes in conversation with the operator regarding your ideas. Forty-five minutes either initiating or simulating changes. The event may last two hours. It may last twenty minutes. Decide for yourself. The infinite variables between different workplaces creates a whole range of possibilities. The only thing that is consistent throughout is the achievement of results.

As far as monitoring is concerned we have looked at various systems as we have progressed, be they Time Observation sheets or CPE, but whatever system you put in place as part of the exercise, there must be good use made of it. Hold meetings to discuss CI, and make sure that they are specific to CI only. Review the information that is coming back to you. Act on areas of concern. Track issues graphically, such as specific changeover times or production concerns.

You will have put in a lot of time and effort to successfully conclude a CI initiative, and if you are serious about continuous improvements, then you, as a Lean Production engineer, must be serious about improving continually. Information gathering just for the sake of it does no one any good.

So, pick up that shovel and move that machine.

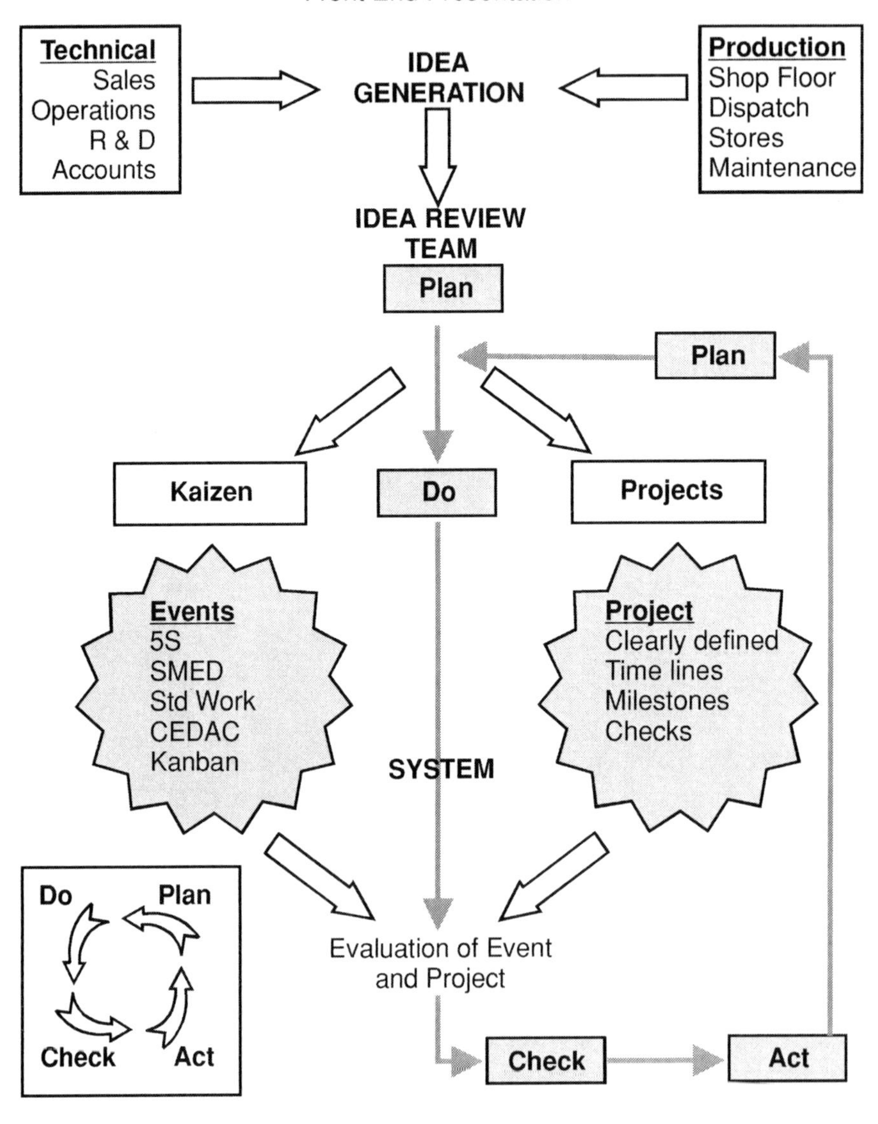
Continuous Improvements System
Front End Presentation
Technical
Sales
Operations
R & D
Accounts
IDEA
GENERATION
Production
Shop Floor
Dispatch
Stores
Maintenance
IDEA REVIEW
TEAM
Plan
Plan
Kaizen
Do
Projects
Events
5S
SMED
Std Work
CEDAC
Kanban
SYSTEM
Project
Clearly defined
Time lines
Milestones
Checks
Do
Plan
Check
Act
Evaluation of Event
and Project
Check
Act

Improvement Initiation Sheet

Department: Area:
Proposed by: Date:
Department Manager:

Proposal:		
Do you consider this to be a kaizen or a project? (Please tick box)	Kaizen	Project
Brief outline:		
Approximate cost:		
Justification (payback and benefits):		
Further actions required:		
Review team's recommendations:		

Kaizen Preparation Check Sheet

Department: Area: Starting date:
Event objectives:

Team Co-ordinator:
Team members: 1. ______ 2. ______
3. ______ 4. ______
5. ______ 6. ______

	Working days to event	Items to be completed by (Give date)	Status (Complete/incomplete)
Inform team of event	>10		
Goals agreed	10		
Area selected	10		
Team and resources selected	10		
Stock available if required	5		
Data collection started	5		
CID Manager signs off	3		
Event starts	0		

Signed by: Initialled

CID Manager:
Engineer responsible:
Team Co-ordinator:

Kaizen Monitor

Department::
Area:
Dates: From: To:

Event objectives:

Team Co-ordinator:

Team members: ________________
____
____
____
____

Results

Comments	Before	After	% Change

Future plans

Aftermath

An often expressed complaint about kaizen events is this :-

'They work well for a few weeks, but then we slip into the ways that we used to work.'

This is true enough. The following graph shows how changeover times traditionally perform:

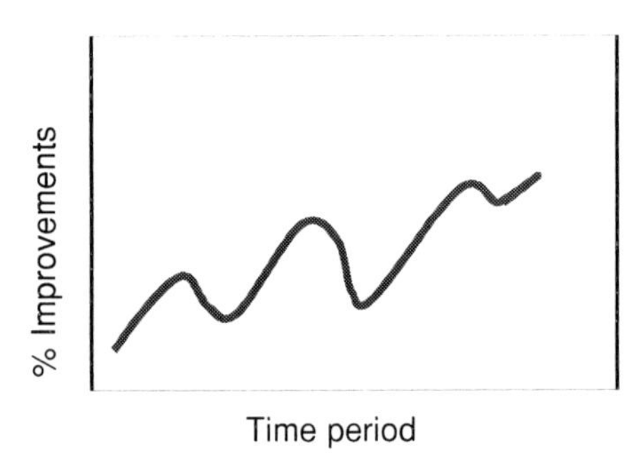

What we are aiming for is this:

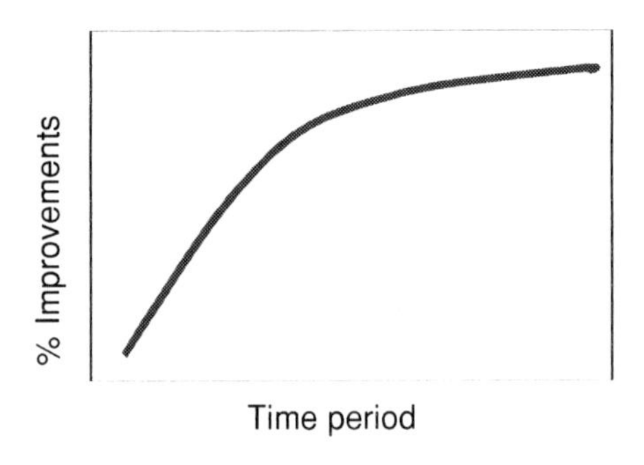

The 80/20 rule applies here. The first 80% is easy to accomplish, but the final 20 takes time and effort.

Once you start to implement some of these philosophies, you need to keep a track not just of the individual components but of the entire Continuous Improvements project. You need to monitor how well your systems are doing. This of course can be accomplished through the use of

CPE. Any problem areas should be highlighted and discovered as part of the ongoing review.

This allows the systems to be monitored at a glance, providing quick and easily understood information. All of this is obvious. This information will also be detailed in the specific areas where the events took place to keep everyone informed about the situation. Once again, obvious and this uses only real information (times, output etc.)

However if you want to judge the feelings of the personnel and obtain an empirical view as to the success of the improvements, then the following is an option.

Quarterly Review

The best way to do this is to carry out a Quarterly Review (every three months). As this should cover the entire workplace, it is very often only the management who have a view of the bigger picture to allow this to happen.

It can be carried out as follows:

The team chosen will be given a small pack containing all aspects of the system to be reviewed and be asked to give their opinion, on a scale of 1 to 5, bad to good, of how they feel the company is performing in a number of key areas. These areas may be:

1. SMED
2. 5S
3. TPM
4. CEDAC
5. FMEA
6. Kanban
7. Standard Work
8. Poka-Yoke

The criteria for these performance indicators will be clearly laid out in advance of the system commencing and will be in use for the entire duration that the system is in place. For example:

Section 1 – SMED

Changeovers are performed for large runs only. They are infrequent and may take over half of a shift to complete.	**1**
There is an awareness of the principles of SMED, however participation is through necessity rather than choice and there is no formal system in place.	**2**
Changeovers are monitored, with standard changeover procedures recorded. Teams are in place to implement SMED but there is a limited amount of success.	**3**
SMED is carried out vigorously. Changeovers occur throughout the day in most areas of the plant.	**4**
Changeovers are carried out within the Single Minutes specified in SMED. Changeovers are a part and parcel of everyday activity within the plant. Everyone in the workforce is aware of the principles of SMED.	**5**

As each manager receives a copy of the criteria they should complete each section, simply by matching up the details contained in the description with their own personal feelings. They should be honest in this. If they are not, then they are only fooling themselves and adversely affecting the companies progress.

Any additional comments would also be beneficial.

Once all of the sheets have been returned, an average can be taken for each of the main areas. From here we can construct a very visual radar chart of the companies progress as felt by the workforce:

Quarterly review chart

To be used alongside CPE figures

Review Date:

Event	Average Score
SMED	3
5S	4
TPM	3
CEDAC	2
FMEA	4
Kanban	1
Standard Work	2
Poka-Yoke	2

Quarterly review radar chart

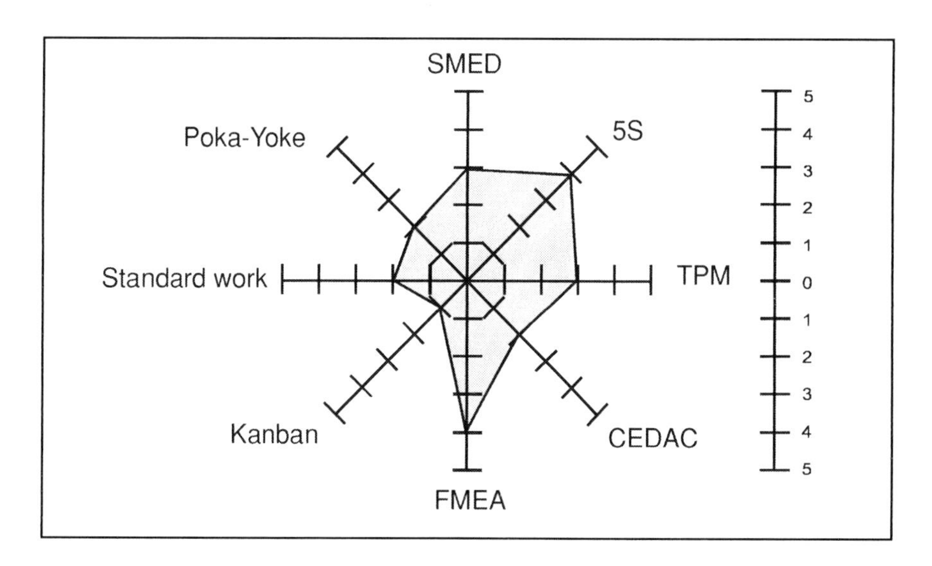